F₁

**Books are to be returned on or before
the last date below**

Elements of Linear Microcircuits

Elements of Linear Microcircuits

T. D. TOWERS, M.B.E., M.A., B.Sc., M.I.E.R.E.
(Director, Newmarket Transistors Ltd.)

LONDON
ILIFFE BOOKS

THE BUTTERWORTH GROUP

ENGLAND
Butterworth & Co (Publishers) Ltd
London: 88 Kingsway, WC2B 6AB

AUSTRALIA
Butterworths Pty Ltd
Sydney: 586 Pacific Highway, NSW 2067
Melbourne: 343 Little Collins Street, 3000
Brisbane: 240 Queen Street, 4000

CANADA
Butterworth & Co (Canada) Ltd
Toronto: 14 Curity Avenue, 374

NEW ZEALAND
Butterworths of New Zealand Ltd
Wellington: 26-28 Waring Taylor Street, 1

SOUTH AFRICA
Butterworth & Co (South Africa) (Pty) Ltd
Durban: 152-154 Gale Street

First Published in 1973 by
Iliffe Books, an imprint
of the Butterworth Group

© Butterworth & Co. (Publishers) Ltd., 1973

ISBN 0 592 00077 X

Printed in England by the Pitman Press, Bath

Preface

During the past decade, linear devices have assumed great importance and are now widely used for radio, television, amplifiers, instrumentation and many other industrial and commercial applications.

The information in this book is based on a series of articles written by the author for Wireless World and is intended to assist bench engineers in research and development laboratories. The book will also be useful to technical college students in electronics at ONC and HNC levels.

Most general-purpose linear microcircuits are operational amplifiers and the first two chapters are devoted to a simple and straightforward explanation of the linear microcircuit and the commercial types which are available. Lists of manufacturers and distributors are given to assist the reader who wishes to obtain linear microcircuits for his own designs.

Separate chapters deal with various types of amplifiers and cover audio amplifiers, r.f. and i.f. amplifiers and wideband amplifiers. These chapters also include directories of types which are currently available.

The last four chapters cover applications and include typical circuit diagrams for the many equipments which can be constructed using linear microcircuits. These include voltage regulators, a.m. and f.m. radio receivers and television receivers.

T. D. Towers

Contents

CHAPTER 1

What a linear microcircuit is, how it is made and packaged

What are these microcircuits that have revolutionized circuit design? In widest terms, they are a sort of supercomponent consisting of a number of circuit elements inseparably associated in a small package. In the ultimate they reduce the equipment designer's job to just fitting together a few prefabricated circuit blocks instead of designing a large complex of separate discrete components. No longer need the electronics experimenter puzzle out the design of a two-transistor 'Ridler' d.c. coupled pair for his tape replay amplifier; he just buys a ready built microcircuit.

Linear and digital: the difference

There are two classes of microcircuits (often called integrated circuits or just i.cs): digital and linear. Digitals are designed for on/off switching applications and provide the equipment designer with a range of complete logic elements, such as AND, OR, NAND, NOR gates, flip-flops and some extremely complex computer-type sub-systems. Linear i.cs are for applications where the output is in some way proportional to the input, and they provide the designer with ready-made d.c., a.f., r.f. and wideband amplifiers.

Digital microcircuits became generally commercially available in the mid-1960s and have been exhaustively discussed in the technical press since then. Linear i.cs did not become readily available until much later, and are only now finding wide use.

Linear microcircuits can be 'multiple-purpose' or 'single-purpose'. Multiple-purpose units are gain-blocks which can be externally pin-programmed to perform a large variety of different circuit functions (usually by fitting different feedback networks). The archetype of these is the operational amplifier or op. amp. This is a very high gain d.c.-coupled amplifier with a response which is completely defined by feedback. It was the earliest linear microcircuit to become generally available and is the best known.

Most circuit designers prefer single-purpose microcircuits, which are complete in themselves and do not need additional circuits designed around before they can be used (as is the case with multiple-purpose linear i.cs). Fortunately, more and more single-purpose linear i.cs are coming on the market, ranging from a simple package of a matched pair of transistors up to a complete 100-W audio power amplifier.

1

Early developments

Before we look at current methods of microcircuit manufacture, it is of interest to look back over the past three decades at the landmarks in their evolution. Up until World War II, the normal methods of assembling electronic equipment was to mount all the heavier components on some form of chassis, and then interconnect them with point-to-point wiring, either directly or via tag boards.

The first major move towards present-day microcircuits began with the miniature proximity fuses developed for the nose-caps of artillery shells in World War II. These radio-controlled fuses were closely packed assemblies using special valves, but the technique never spread into large scale commercial use because of the bulky valve needed for amplification.

The development of microelectronics really started with the invention of the transistor in 1948. This got rid of the large wasted vacuum space inside the valve, its inefficient heater and the need for a high anode voltage. Assemblies could now be

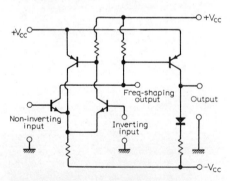

Fig. 1.   Circuit of 1962 linear silicon integrated circuit (Texas Instruments SN521 operational amplifier).

much smaller, but they were still only scaled-down versions of the old point-to-point inter-wiring of discrete components.

In the late 1940s, Sargrove in England started a move away from point-to-point wiring. He pioneered a development in which a radio receiver was built on a ceramic substrate on which resistors and intercomponent wirings were printed and fired rather than separately mounted. This was one of the earlier experiments in the integration of circuitry, but in spite of it, point-to-point wiring continued unopposed.

Later printed circuit boards (more correctly printed wiring boards) became a commercial reality, and this form of integrated wiring provided another big step towards commercial microelectronics.

The 1950s also saw many different approaches to miniaturization, apart from assembling conventional miniature components on a small printed circuit board. They gave rise to names like 'Cordwood', 'Tinkertoy', 'Micromodule' and '2D', which are now largely of historical interest only. Details can be found in books such as 'Microelectronics' by E. Keonjian. (McGraw Hill, 1963.)

All these forms of microminiature assemblies developed in the 1950s were more expensive than the standard printed circuit board and they were only used in equipment where cost was not the governing element, military equipment for instance.

Today's microcircuits

In 1958 a development occurred which changed the whole face of things. Kilby of Texas Instruments came up with an interconnected assembly of resistors and transistors made by diffusion in tiny silicon chips. The true monolithic silicon integrated circuit (s.i.c.) had been born. The first of these was a mesa-type r.t.l. (resistor transistor logic) bistable and it used only two chips interconnected by bonding wires in a single package.

In 1960 the celebrated Fairchild planar process for manufacturing transistors was developed which gave a strong impetus to the production of monolithic s.i.cs. Early units were the easiest-to-make digital types such as the 1961 Texas Instruments Series-51 r.t.l. But linear s.i.cs were not long in arriving. By 1962, the Texas Series-52 linear i.cs were on the market. Typical of these was the SN521 general-purpose single-chip 62dB differential amplifier the circuit of which is given in Fig. 1.

In the linear field, however, the general use of linear s.i.cs can be said to have started with the now well known Fairchild μA709 op. amp. which came on the market in quantity in 1965. Since then there has been a proliferation of multiple-purpose linear amplifiers, particularly of the operational amplifier type.

But the linear s.i.cs available by the mid-1960s did not get the immediate wide usage that their high technical specifications invited. This was partly because production was small and the cost was much higher than a designer could achieve by using conventional component circuitry. Also, run-of-the-mill circuit designers were not skilled at using wideband, high-gain operational amplifier blocks for general purpose circuitry. They would rather have had low-cost single-purpose units.

In this climate, significant developments began along different lines. Techniques developed for producing prefabricated assemblies of resistors, capacitors and interconnections by printing on ceramics (thick film) or vacuum evaporation on glass (thin film) were married to special miniature semiconductor devices suitable for attaching to such substrates. Out of this marriage came the hybrid active linear microcircuit, which had advantages over monolithics in some areas. The two main ones that the hybrid could be fabricated economically in small batches and that single-purpose units could be made up readily.

By the end of the 1960s, many semiconductor manufacturers had gone into monolithic s.i.cs. Cheap standard multiple-purpose linear i.cs had become widely available, but there were not many standard single-purpose units around. You could get a special s.i.c. custom built, but you would have to use very large quantities for it to be economic. As a result, many custom hybrid houses had sprung up, using thick and thin film techniques, to serve the smaller-run equipment manufacturer who could not use the existing standard monoliths and was too small to have a special monolith built for him. Almost as a by-product, these hybrid houses also put on the market standard commercial single-purpose linears.

It is anybody's guess how the demand for linear microcircuits will divide itself up in the future between standard single-purpose, standard multiple-purpose, and custom-built units. One estimate is that in the 1970s linear applications will be met 50% by off-the-shelf single-purpose standards, 25% by multiple-purpose standards, and 25% by custom specials. As to how far the units will be monolithic and how far hybrid, again there is much doubt. The chances are that most multiple-purpose standards will be monoliths, most custom units hybrid, and single-purpose units a mixture of monolithic and hybrid.

No reference has been made so far to m.o.s.t. (metal oxide semiconductor technique) microcircuits which use f.e.ts (field effect transistors) instead of bipolar transistors as the basic circuit elements diffused into silicon chips. They are cheaper to produce than bipolar monoliths, and have already found wide use in low-cost digital applications. However, they are not as yet well suited directly to linear applications, and will not be discussed further here.

As to hybrid technologies, thin film is gradually being phased out for cost and technical reasons, and most hybrids are now thick film.

3

Monolithic silicon circuit manufacture

Manufacturing monolithic s.i.cs is a highly complex business and many books have been produced on the subject. If you are seeking detailed information, you should consult one of the standard texts, such as Motorola's 'Integrated Circuits—Design Principle and Fabrication', edited by M. Warner (McGraw Hill, 1965). In this chapter we will give only a brief outline of how s.i.cs are made.

The process starts with an ingot, usually about 250mm (10in) long and 25mm (1in) diameter, of highly refined single-crystal silicon, shown in Fig.2(a). The ingot is sawn up into thin slices of which one is shown at Fig.2(b), and the s.i.cs are made in these slices.

As shown in the enlarged view of a single slice in Fig.2(c), a large number of identical circuits are formed in a regular pattern. Various techniques are used, such as high-temperature diffusion of impurity gases into the slice, selective surface etching of photoresist masking, formation of protective 'glass' (silicon oxide) surface layers, and deposition of metallic interconnections and lead bonding pads on the surface by vacuum evaporation (thin film) techniques. Depending on the area of the individual circuit in the pattern, a single slice typically produces anything from 200 and 2000 identical integrated circuits at the one time.

The slice is next scribed along the dividing lines between the circuits and broken up into individual units. A single circuit then finally appears as at Fig.2(d)—enlarged—in the shape of a square chip between 0.5mm (0.020in) and 1.25mm (0.050in) across with visible metallization on the surface.

This chip is packaged by bonding it face-up on a support such as the multi-lead TO-5 header shown in Fig.2(e), with the metallized bonding pads visible on the face. Connections are then made from the header leads to the pads by gold or aluminium wire about 0.025mm (0.001in) diameter. After being tested, the package is sealed. In the example shown, a metal top cap is fitted by welding round the rim.

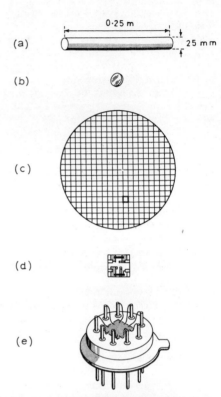

Fig. 2. Construction of silicon integrated circuits: (a) basic silicon crystal ingot from which process starts; (b) thin slice (wafer) cut from ingot; (c) enlarged view of slice after processing produces large number of identical circuits inside the silicon formed by repeated diffusion, oxidation, and selective etching with final evaporation of surface metallization for interconnections and bonding pads; (d) one of many single-circuit chips obtained by scribing and cracking the complete slice, and (e) individual circuit chip mounted on header with connections to header leads.

From this necessarily brief summary, it should be evident that the basic element in a monolithic s.i.c. is a very small processed thin chip of silicon about the area of a grain of sugar. This makes it clear why high-power dissipation presents a major problem in s.i.cs, because of the difficulty in getting the heat away from the tiny chip. Normally, temperatures inside the chip must be kept below about 150 to 180°C and because of its small size it is hard to dissipate much power without exceeding this limit. This also explains why most of the commonly available s.i.cs have a power rating somewhere round 100 to 500mW (very much the same as a single transistor), and also why most of the high power linear microcircuits on the market tend to use the hybrid fabrication to be described below.

Thick film hybrid fabrication

The assembly of a thick film hybrid starts with a smooth ceramic (aluminium oxide) blank substrate, typically about 25mm (1in) square and 0.375 to 0.875mm (0.015 to 0.035in) thick, as shown in Fig.3(a).

On to this ceramic (which is an insulator) a matrix of passive circuit elements is screen printed and fired, just like the decorations on a piece of pottery, as shown in Fig.3(b). This produces an identical pattern of resistors, capacitors, insulating layers and metal interconnection runs and bonding pads (the last for attaching discrete components and external leads) in each cell of the matrix.

The large substrate is then scribed along the cell dividing lines and cracked up into individual small circuit substrates. One of these is shown enlarged in Fig.3(c). The next step is to attach any subminiature discrete components required, such as the transistor shown in Fig.3(d), and the final substrate preparation is the attaching of external leads shown in Fig.3(e).

After being tested, the hybrid circuit is encapsulated in some form of protective

package, as shown in Fig. 3(f). It can be seen that the dissipating semiconductors can be dispersed over a relatively wider area than is possible in an s.i.c. chip so

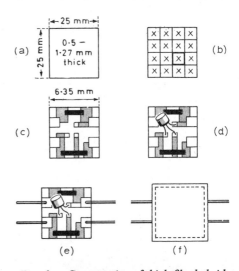

Fig. 3. Construction of thick-film hybrid microcircuits: (a) Starting ceramic substrate; (b) number of identical R, C and conductor networks printed and fired on substrate; (c) single circuit substrate scribed and cracked from complete multiple-unit substrate; (d) discrete components such as transistors attached to substrate. (e) Leadout wires attached; (f) circuit encapsulated in protective package.

higher power dissipation is possible. On the other hand, it must also be clear that the overall package size will tend to be larger for hybrids.

The packaging of a microcircuit is of importance not only because it is all that the user sees of the device, but also because it has such an important bearing on cost and reliability.

Microcircuit packaging; the problems

Just as with transistors, microcircuit packages are of two basic types, 'hermetic' (metal or ceramic and glass) and 'non-hermetic' (plastic). Non-hermetic are much cheaper than hermetic, but have not yet reached the stage where they can be regarded as satisfactory in extremes of temperature and humidity. Thus in high reliability applications, hermetic packages are the rule. Initially only hermetic packages were accepted for professional use, but recently plastics have improved so much that they are creeping in for the less demanding applications.

In commercial linear microcircuits, you will therefore find three grades in the market: (a) *Entertainment* or *Consumer,* suitable for use from 0 to 70°C and in low humidity environments (and almost always non-hermetic), (b) *Industrial,* suitable for use from −20 to +100°C and in medium high humidity (mostly hermetic), and (c) *Military* for −55 to +125°C and high humidity environments (until now always hermetic).

Unfortunately for the user, package standardization for microcircuits is a long way off. We are not yet in the comforting climate of transistors where you can take the same JEDEC standard TO-5 outline device from several different manufacturers and find that the case sizes varied by only a few thousandths of an inch and that the standard emitter-base-collector numbering of leads round the can obtained in every case.

For linear microcircuits at the time of writing there are over 700 different shapes, sizes and lead configurations available. In this chaos of packages offered, however, some trends are beginning to make themselves clear.

Monolithic s.i.c. packages show more standardization than hybrids because they have been around longer. But packages which have reached some acceptance for monoliths have had to be severely modified to encompass the generally larger hybrid element.

With regard to outlines, packages fall into four main classes: (1) low-power packages with leads to be inserted through

circuit boards and soldered on the copper side; (2) low-power packages designed to be mounted directly on the copper side with leads attached flat to the metallization by soldering or welding; (3) medium-power packages with integral heat sinks for printed circuit board mounting; and (4) high-power packages designed for attachment to substantial metal chassis or heat sinks.

Low-power through-board-mounting packages

The most common low-power through-board-mounting microcircuit package is the *dual-in-line,* abbreviated to d.i.l. for the hermetic version and d.i.p. for the non-hermetic or plastic version Fig.4(a) shows the main dimensions of the most

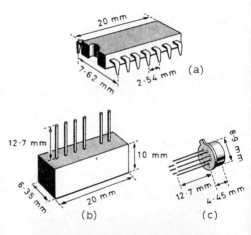

Fig. 4. *Typical common low-power linear microcircuit packages for attachment to non-copperside of printed circuit board: (a) Dual-in-line; (b) single-in-line; (c) multilead TO-5.*

common package, the 14-lead dual-in-line. Variants of the package may have anything from 4 to 24 leads or more. The interlead spacing of 2.54mm (0.1in) in the line of leads is standard (to allow conductor runs between the lead lands on

6

the board). The inter-row spacing of 7.62mm (0.3in) is standard for monolithic s.i.cs, but, for the generally larger hybrid, other spacings such as 15mm (0.6in) are common.

Dual-in-lines are not easy to unsolder from circuit boards for servicing, and there is growing up another package style for through-board mounting which is easier to unsolder. This is the *single-in-line,* of which an example will be found in Fig.4(b). This s.i.l. can be thought of as half of a dual-in-line with the leads straightened into the plane of the device. It too, like the d.i.l., tends to use lead spacings of 2.54mm (0.1in), and is more common in hybrids than monoliths.

Historically the earliest monoliths were developed by semiconductor manufacturers and it was natural that they should package them in modified transistor cases. Fig.4(c) gives an illustration of the multilead TO-5 which may have anything from six to twelve leads. Because of the close lead spacing and the difficulty of removal from a printed circuit board, it is now not very popular with designers.

Low-power copper-side mounting packages

In these days of double-sided printed circuit boards and the demand for space

saving, several packages have been developed for attaching to the copper side of the board. Two are fairly standard.

The *flat pack* shown in Fig.5(a) was developed by Texas Instruments for their early s.i.cs. With the general adoption of the dual-in-line package described earlier, users who wanted to mount them on the copper side of the board dressed their leads out flat as shown in Fig.5(b). This gave rise to the *ready-to-reflow* dual-in-line modification which manufacturers are now prepared to supply.

Medium-power microcircuit packages

The packages so far discussed usually cannot dissipate more than a few hundred milliwatts. Other packages had to be developed for higher powers, particularly in the linear field. These tend to fall into two main groups: (a) items designed for powers up to about 5W without any special substantial external heat sinking, and (b) high-power packages capable of dissipating up to 50 or 100W.

In the first, medium-power, category, several packages will be met with. Semiconductor manufacturers, accustomed to standard two-pin TO-3 outline power transistors, developed a multi-pin version of this outline, of which Fig.6(a) shows a typical example. On a printed circuit board this can dissipate up to about 2W (and on a substantial heatsink 10W).

Another transistor case used for medium-power microcircuits is the multilead TO-8 transistor package, of which Fig.6(b) is an example. This has twelve pins arranged in a square, but a sixteen-pin version is also available. This package can dissipate up to about 1W in free air and about 2.5W clipped to a substantial heat sink.

A different approach to a medium-power package is the integral *heat sink.* Fairly typical of this is the package sketched in Fig.6(c). This is really a dual-in-line with the leads dressed for reflow soldering and with a strip of metal

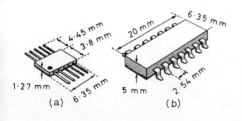

Fig. 5. Typical low-power linear microcircuit packages for attachment to copper side of printed circuit board: (a) Flat pack; (b) ready-to-reflow dual-in-line with preformed leads.

7

inside extending from one end for better removal of heat from the chip Permissible power dissipation can be

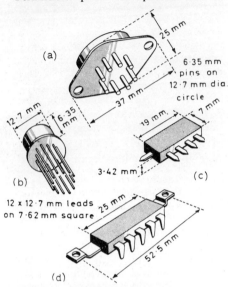

(a)

25 mm

6·35 mm pins on 12·7 mm dia. circle

37 mm

12·7 mm

6·35 mm

(b)

12 x 12·7 mm leads on 7·62mm square

19 mm

3·42 mm

(c)

7 mm

25 mm

52·5 mm

(d)

Fig. 6. Examples of medium-power linear microcircuit packages; (a) Modified multilead TO-3 power transistor package (2-5W); (b) modified multilead TO-8 intermediate power transistor package (1-2W); (c) modified dual-in-line with integral tongued heat sink (1W); (d) modified dual-in-line with integral heat sink for bolting to chassis (3W).

increased by soldering the metal tongue to board metallization or some area of metal. Packages like these are typically capable of dissipations up to 1W.

The power dissipation capability of integral heat sink package can be extended by making provisions for bolting to a metal heat sink. One well known example of this is the *chassis-mounting integral heat sink* given at Fig.6(d). This package is used for a linear monolithic amplifier with a power output capability of 3W audio, which has been widely marketed in the United Kingdom.

High-power microcircuit packages

Package design becomes a critical problem when we come to linear i.c.s. capable of handling more than a few watts, whether they be monolithic or hybrid. At the time of writing no standard packages have been evolved, but the main features to be expected in such packages can be seen in the illustrative example of Fig.7. This is a 50-W high-quality audio

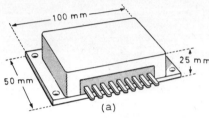

100 mm

25 mm

50 mm

(a)

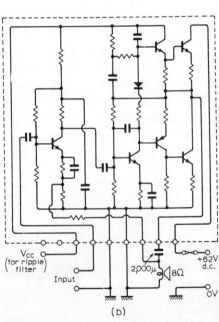

Vcc (for ripple filter)

Input

2,000µ

8Ω

+62V d.c.

0V

(b)

Fig. 7. Typical commercial example of high-power linear microcircuit (Sanken Electric SI-1050A, 50Watt Hi-fi power amplifier). (a) Package: (b) hybrid circuit.

8

amplifier. In the casing outline at Fig.7(a), you can see that it is a fairly substantial package, 100 × 50 × 25mm (4 × 2 × 1in), with flanges for bolting to a chassis or heat sink. The terminals are stout pins issuing from one side of the package, to which connections can be made by soldering or by crimped-tag flying leads. The amplifier is of the quasi complementary class-B type and the circuit used is shown in Fig.7(b). The main power-dissipating elements are the two output transistors. Some expertise is required to mount these in the package to ensure the most efficient removal of the heat—quite a problem when you realise that the power transistor chips are asked to dissipate internally 30W apiece.

Sockets for microcircuits

In the early days of transistors, when designers were a little uncertain how to handle them, it was common to fit sockets for them on printed circuit boards. We see the same development with microcircuits, and there is a lot to be said for it.

Sockets for standard dual-in-line, single-in-line and multilead TO-5 packages are nowadays fairly readily available from electronics distributors. Apart from distributors, some firms specialize in the supply of microcircuit sockets, such as Jermyn Industries in the U.K. and Augat or Barnes in the U.S.A. (with agents in the U.K.).

If you are buying microcircuit sockets, remember that they come in two types: "test" sockets specially designed for continuous repetitive use, and "production" sockets for once (or occasionally twice) use in equipment. Obviously production sockets will be cheaper than the test type.

Availability of Linear Microcircuits

From this preliminary look at the linear microcircuit field, it should be evident that nowadays the designer can look to a large commercial armoury of such circuits around which to build his equipment. As later articles in this series will show, he will find linear i.c.s. for applications in frequencies from d.c. to 1,000MHz, powers from 0.1mW to 100W and gains from 0dB(× 1) to 120dB (× 1,000,000).

CHAPTER 2

Survey of types and selection

If you are going to use linear microcircuits effectively in your designs, you should know what are available on the market, where to get them and what precautions to take in procuring them.

Supply sources for linear microcircuits

Linear i.cs come on to the U.K. market from all over the world; the main manufacturing sources are: U.S.A., U.K., Western Europe, and Far East (Japan, Hong Kong, Korea and Taiwan).

U.K. products can be obtained direct from the manufacturers or from electronics distributors. Microcircuits of overseas manufacture reach the British user mostly through subsidiaries of the prime manufacturers, although more and more agents and distributors are handling imported linear devices direct from the overseas sources.

To help you in your search Table 1 gives a list of the major U.K. manufacturers of off-the-shelf linear microcircuits.

To complete the picture, Table 2 sets out the major overseas manufacturers (apart from those already appearing in the U.K. list).

It is impracticable to give details of the many distributors handling linear microcircuits, but most good distributors now hold stocks of what are rapidly becoming standard items. The sort of thing you will find is reflected in the catalogue of one U.K. national distributor currently offering a standard μA709 op. amp., a μA710 d.c. comparator, a μA711 dual d.c. comparator, a 3-W audio power amplifier and a 2 to 13V, 100mA d.c. power supply regulator module.

Microcircuit numbering codes

If you are new to the microcircuit game, you will find yourself confused and often frustrated by the huge variety of type numbers given to commercial units. Cynics have said that the numbers put on devices by manufacturers are designed to confuse. There might be some truth in this if we are to judge by the now-legendary '709', which you could come across under about a hundred different type numbers. You will find it easier to make your way in the world of microcircuits if you know and can recognize the different numbering systems you will come across.

There are three main systems current

in the U.K.: 'House-code', 'Pro-electron' and 'Military'.

House-code numbers

Linear microcircuit manufacturers generally use their own in-house coding systems. For their commercially available off-the-shelf units they tend to adopt a coding which is identifiable with the company. For example, Newmarket Transistors uses the letters NMC (Newmarket Micro Circuit) followed by a three-digit numerical reference for its standard range. But, in addition, most manufacturers also use a separate 'private' in-house coding for the special microcircuits they do not make generally commercially available. You may occasionally come across such private numbers in technical articles and may find it difficult to identify the manufacturer from the code alone. Table 3 gives a list of the more common commercial house-codings which can be readily identified.

Obviously the user would like a common number for interchangeable microcircuits, whatever the source, and the Pro-electron system to be described below is a useful move in this direction.

Pro-electron numbering

Pro-electron is an international organization in Belgium with which manufacturers register their microcircuits (and incidentally many other semiconductors and valves) according to a carefully designed coding system.

So far as linear microcircuits are concerned, the standard type designation code comprises three letters followed by three numerals, e.g. TAA263. This block of six elements breaks down into three sections, T . . . AA26 . . . 3, and each of the three sections has a special significance.

The initial letter T is always used for purely linear microcircuits but there is provision in the system for the initial letter U to be used for combined linear-digital circuits. Thus the code for a linear microcircuit always starts with T or U.

The middle two letters and two numerals comprise a serial registration number. In this, the letters start from AA and will continue through BA, CA up to ZA. The two digits in the middle section run from 10 through to 99.

The last figure, i.e. the third one in the full number, gives an indication of the operative temperature range for which the circuit can be used, and has the following meaning: $0 =$ no temperature range indicated, $1 = 0$ to $+70°C$, $2 = -55$ to $+125°C$, $3 = -10$ to $+85°C$, $4 = +15$ to $+55°C$, $5 = -25$ to $+70°C$, and $6 = -40$ to $+85°C$. If a circuit specification is for a wider temperature range, but does not qualify for a higher classification, the figure indicating the narrower temperature range is used.

Although the Pro-electron coding for a linear microcircuit is normally three letters followed by three numerals, a version letter can be added to a type number to indicate a different version of the same type; for instance encapsulated in another package with other interconnections or showing minor differences in ratings or electrical characteristics.

Referring back to the TAA263 mentioned earlier as an example of the Pro-electron coding. Although registered with Pro-electron initially by Philips, any other manufacturer who can produce it to meet the registered specification can use the same number 26, and it is likely that there will be more than one supplier for many of the registered Pro-electron types. At present, however, the position is that most of the Pro-electron-registered linear microcircuits are obtainable only from the manufacturer who initially registered them. As a result, some of the Pro-electron codings have become associated in the minds of users with the originating company.

Military numbering systems

In the United Kingdom, just as valves and transistors for use in government equipments were registered under CV numbers, so microcircuits have been covered by a CN numbering system. For example, the well-known differential voltage comparator, $\mu A710$, is designated CN431T (multi-lead TO-5 version) and CN432F (flat-pack version).

A system is also being developed under which industrial microcircuits will be allotted numbers under the BS9000 scheme.

Cost of linear microcircuits

Until 1969 linear microcircuits were very expensive but in the middle of 1970 a very heavy price slide took place and we experienced a very interesting situation where quite complex microcircuits were down hard on the heels of the price of single transistors. High-quality linear microcircuits can be purchased at one-off prices from about 40p. A welcome situation has thus been reached where the amateur and home experimenter can "try his 'prentice hand" without being unduly out-of-pocket. And all indications are that the price decline is likely to continue, as more and more supplies come on the market.

Points to watch

There are several pitfalls in the path of the buyer of linear microcircuits. The first snare is interchangeability. You can buy a $\mu A709$ operational amplifier from two different manufacturers, each meeting a common data sheet specification, and find that one works well in your circuit and the other does not. This may not be because anything is wrong with either of them, but because they differ materially in parameters not specified in the data sheet. All you can do is to try samples of the different makes and design your circuitry to give equal performance with both. The fact that two 709s from different manufacturers cannot be interchanged with certainty is not surprising when you consider that there is an assembly of 15 transistors and 15 resistors diffused into a tiny chip of silicon in this device.

However closely you study the specification of a microcircuit, you will not find some characteristics that can have a more than marginal influence on its operation in circuit. This is not because the manufacturer wishes to conceal them from you. It is because they are not measured on a production basis, and are held to be secondary characteristics that do not materially affect the operation of the device in the application for which it is designed.

Remember that it is almost impossible to produce a true low-frequency transistor in the sense of the old germanium alloy transistors when you fabricate by planar techniques. Cut-off frequencies below 100MHz are most unusual in planar types. This means that you are dealing with a compact circuit with potentialities of high gain at very high frequencies. Because of these "unspoken" specifications, you can run into enormous difficulties with high-frequency instability in low-frequency circuits.

Another point to be wary of is the question of 'pin compatability'. What this means is . . . look carefully at the lead-out pin-numbering of your microcircuit in relation to the internal circuitry to ensure that an alternative you are trying is an exact drop-in replacement.

If you buy microcircuits direct from a reputable manufacturer, you can be fairly sure they will meet specification. However, the semiconductor industry is such that units can come on the market via other outlets which may have the proper code number marked on them but may not meet the full data sheet specification. If you use such orphans, you must have the facility for testing them against specification.

Since it can be quite difficult to test a linear i.c. satisfactorily, some guidance will be given in later articles how to set about this.

If you are seriously contemplating using linear microcircuits, there is a lot to be said for getting some practical handling experience. Make up a working circuit using

---

Table 1
U.K. manufacturers of off-the-shelf linear microcircuits
A.B. Electronics Co., *Apemworks, St. Albans Road, Watford, Herts.*
Erie Electronics Ltd., *South Denes, Gt. Yarmouth.*
Ferranti Ltd., *Gem Mill, Chadderton, Oldham, Lancs.*
Marconi-Elliott-Microelectronics Ltd., *Witham, Essex.*
Mullard Ltd., *Mullard House, Torrington Place, London W.C.1.*
Newmarket Transistors Ltd., *Exning Road, Newmarket, Suffolk.*
Plessey Microelectronics Ltd., *Cheney Manor, Swindon, Wilts.*
S. G. S. (U.K.) Ltd., *Planar House, Walton Street, Aylesbury, Bucks.*
Texas Instruments Ltd., *Manton Lane, Bedford.*

Table 2
Overseas manufacturers whose off-the-shelf linear microcircuits are available in the U.K.
Amelco Semiconductors, *1300 Terra Bella Avenue, Mountain View, California, U.S.A.*
Beckman Instruments Inc., Helipot Div., *2500 Harbour Blvd., Fullerton, California, U.S.A.*
Fairchild Semiconductors, *313 Fairchild Drive, Mountain View, California, U.S.A.*
General Electric Company, *Northern Concourse Building, Northern Lights, Syracuse, New York, U.S.A.*
General Instrument Corp., *600 West John St., Hicksville, New York, U.S.A.*
ITT Semiconductors, *3301 Electronics Way, West Palm Beach, Florida, U.S.A.*
Mitsubishi Electric Corp., *1 Shuga-Ike, Ojika, Itami-Shi, Hygo-Ken, Japan.*
Motorola Semiconductor Products, Inc., *5005 E. McBowell Rd., Phoenix, Arizona, U.S.A.*
National Semiconductor Corp., *2975 San Ysidro Way, Santa Clara, California, U.S.A.*
Philips Gloelampenfabrieken, *Building BFP, Eindhoven, Netherlands.*
RCA, Electronic Components, *Somerville, New Jersey, U.S.A.*
Raytheon Company, *350 Ellis Street, Mountain View, California, U.S.A.*
Sanken Electric Co., *1-22-8 Nishi, Ikebukuro, Toshima-Ku, Tokyo, Japan.*
Siemens Aktiengesellschaft, *Balanstrasse 73, 8000 Munich 8, West Germany.*
Signetics Corp., *811 East Argues Avenue, Sunnyvale, California, U.S.A.*
Siliconix Inc., *1140 W. Evelyn Avenue, Sunnyvale, California, U.S.A.*
Sescosem, *101 Boulevard Murat, Paris, 16e, France.*
Telefunken A.G., *Postfach 1042, 7100 Heilbron/Neckar, West Germany.*
Tokyo Shibaura Electric Co., *1 Komuka Toshiba Cho, Kawasaki, Japan.*
Transitron Electronic Corp., *168-182 Albion St., Wakefield, Massachusetts, U.S.A.*

Table 3

House code prefixes

CA	= R.C.A.	PC	= General Instrument
L	= S.G.S.	RC	= Raytheon
LH	= National Semiconductors	RM	= Raytheon
LM	= National Semiconductors	S	= Signetics
M	= Mitsubishi	SE	= Signetics
MC	= Motorola	SFC	= Sescosem
MIC	= I.T.T.	SI	= Sanken
N	= Signetics	SL	= Plessey
NC	= General Instrument	SN	= Texas Instruments
NE	= Signetics	TDC	= Transitron
NH	= National Semiconductors	TOA	= Transitron
NMC	= Newmarket Transistors	TVR	= Transitron
PA	= General Electric (U.S.A.)	μA	= Fairchild

a linear microcircuit. The old adage about an ounce of practice is almost truer with microcircuits than with anything else in electronics.

Further reading

Manufacturer's application notes, data sheets and catalogues:

'Linear Integrated Circuit D.A.T.A. Book', Computing and software Inc., 32 Lincoln Ave, Grange, New Jersey 07050, U.S.A.

'Microelectronics Year Book', Shaw Publishing Co., London.

'The Applications of Linear Microcircuits', Fairchild Semi-conductors.

'Linear Integrated Circuit Applications Handbook', Marconi Elliott Microelectronics.

'The Application of Linear Microcircuits', S.G.S.

'Linear Applications', Signetics.

'Linear Integrated Circuit Fundamentals', R.C.A.

I. Eimbinder, 'Linear Integrated Circuits: Theory and Applications', Wiley.

I. Eimbinder, 'Designing with Linear Microcircuits', Wiley.

A. J. McEvoy and L. McNamara, 'Practical Integrated Circuits', Butterworth.

The following articles using linear integrated circuits have appeared in *Wireless World:*

P. J. Forrest, 'I.Cs in Communication Equipment', Jan. 67, p.23.

A. J. McEvoy, 'Integrated Circuit Stereo Mixer and Pre-amplifiers', July 67, p.314.

G. J. Newnham, 'FM Tuner Using Integrated Circuits', June 69, p.250.

F. C. Evans, 'Frequency Divider with Variable Tuning', July 69, p.324.

G. B. C. Harrap, 'Driver Amplifier for Pen Recorder', Aug. 69, p.379.

G. J. Newnham, 'R.F. Amplifier for F.M. Tuner', Nov.69, p.525.

J. M. A. Wade, 'I.C. Driver for Power Amplifier', Nov. 69, p.530.

A. Basak, 'Constant Amplitude Modulator', Nov. 69, p.530.

D. Bollen, 'A Thermistor Hygrometer', Dec. 69, p.557.

R. Hirst, 'The Future of Linear I.Cs, Jan. 70, p.6.

A. E. Crump, 'Instrumentation Amplifier', Feb. 70, p.70.

M. V. Dromgoole, 'Op. Amp. A. C. Millivoltmeter', Feb. 70, p.75.

J. Bryant, 'Linear Integrated Circuits', Feb. 70, p.75.

L. Nelson Jones, 'Integrated Circuit Stereo Pre-Amplifier', July 70, p.312.

P. Williams, 'Sinusoidal Oscillator for High Temperature', July 70, p.332.

G. B. Clayton 'Operational Amplifiers'.
1. 'Device Characteristics', Feb. 69, p.54.
2. 'Compensation Techniques', Mar. 69, p.130.
3. 'Applications', Apr. 69, p.154.
4. 'Applications', May 69, p.213.
5. 'Applications', June 69, p.270.
6. 'Integrators and Differentiators', July 69, p.332.
7. 'Voltage Comparators and Multi-vibrators', Aug. 69, p.384.
8. 'Selection of Practical Amplifiers', Sept. 69, p.429.
9. 'Practical Circuits', Oct. 69, p.482.
10. 'A Triangular Square-wave Generator', Dec. 69, p.586.

CHAPTER 3

Handling and safety precautions

Microcircuits (especially monolithic) are physically robust but electrically fragile. This chapter outlines precautions careful engineers commonly take in using them. The precautions apply equally to linear and digital circuits. Old hands may cut corners but beginners should observe all the precautions, initially at least.

Whatever kind of microcircuit is being used, and however experienced you are, always get hold of the device data sheet and study it till you understand it in detail, before you set to work.

Storing

If you do not use a microcircuit immediately you receive it, see that you store it carefully. This means avoiding extremes of temperature and humidity, and chemicals; or more simply, keeping it cool, dry and clean. If the microcircuits arrive in special protective package frames, keep these on until just before use.

When you do get out a microcircuit to fit into circuit, do not just leave it lying loose around the bench, where the pins or leads can get distorted. A useful trick is to keep a sheet of expanded polystyrene on which you can temporarily store the unit in safety by pushing its leads into the polystyrene.

Handling

As remarked earlier, microcircuits are physically robust. Even so do not handle them roughly. Generally units have leads designed to withstand pulls up to 1 lb for 0.5mm diameter, 2 lb for 0.7mm, 4 lb for 1.27mm and 10 lb above this. Even so do not pull on the leads unnecessarily.

Most microcircuit leads have diameters between 0.4 and 0.7mm and you should take care when you bend them. A good rule is not to bend the lead nearer than 0.8mm to the body of the device. This is particularly important where the lead issues from the body through a glass-to-metal seal.

If the leads accidentally get twisted out of shape, you should dress them carefully back into shape with a pair of small, long-nosed half-round pliers. Where you are handling large numbers of units with displaced leads, you can buy a lead-straightening jig to do the job safely without skilled hands.

Manufacturers aim for indelible code markings on their packages. However, if you are using a large number of different types, test the printing with your finger tip. If you find it liable to rub off, handle the unit so that the markings are not accidentally erased.

Modern microcircuits are so robust that you are unlikely to cause damage if you drop them, except that you may distort the leads. You can therefore handle them with the same care you would resistors, capacitors and other similar encapsulated components.

Mounting

How you mount a microcircuit in circuit depends very much on whether you are just using one experimentally, are making a few hand-assembled equipments, or are involved in large-scale production.

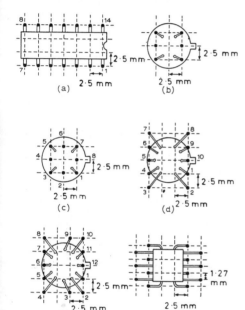

Fig.1. How the leads of microcircuit packages can be dressed to conform to an 2.5 × 2.5mm matrix (a) dual -in-line (b to e) multilead TO-5, (f) flat-pack. Note that additional holes, spaced at 1.27mm are required.

For preliminary bench experiments you can solder the leads to tag strips. But many microcircuits have such short and closely spaced leads that this is impracticable. One alternative is to solder the leads to terminal pins pushed into the selected holes in pre-punched 'Bakelite' boards such as the well known 'Lektrokit' and 'Veroboard'. Another alternative is the 'S-dec' solderless breadboard assembly.

More methodical workers mount their microcircuits with the leads threaded through the grid of holes in Lektrokit or Veroboard. Because the device leads are so closely spaced, the only suitable boards are those with a matrix of holes on a 0.1 √ 0.1 grid. Two board thicknesses are commonly available, 1.5 and 3mm. You will find that the short, 1.5 and 12mm, leads found in some microcircuits may not allow enough lead to project through to make a satisfactory connection underneath the 3mm board.

Three microcircuit package outlines are virtually standard. These are the dual-in-line, the multilead TO-5 and the flatpack as discussed in chapter 1.

Only in the case of the dual-in-line are the leads (spaced at 2.5mm on two parallel lines 7.6mm apart) capable of being fitted directly through the holes on a 2.5mm grid board. The dual-in-line thus mounts easily as in Fig. 1(a), or, if you wish, you can purchase dual-in-line mounting sockets.

When we come to the multilead TO-5, difficulties arise because the leadout positions do not match a 2.5mm grid. This means re-dressing the leads as shown for 6-, 8-, 10-, and 12-lead versions in Fig. 1. Experimentally it is usual to thread 6mm lengths of heat-resisting impregnated glass fibre sleeving over the leads to space the package off the board. Some manufacturers supply their multilead TO-5 devices with leads already dressed to a 2.5mm grid spacing.

If you do not want to bother with the fiddling adjustment of the TO 5 multileads, you can buy small plastic adapter pads with guide holes which steer the leads into the right configuration. Sockets for multilead TO-5 devices are also available for use with printed circuit boards, but most of these unfortunately feed the leads straight through so that there is still the difficulty of mating the socket pins to the board matrix.

The flat-pack is probably the most difficult package to handle experimentally. It is really designed to be mounted by welding or reflow-soldering the flat ribbon leads direct to metallization on one side of a printed-circuit board.

The difficulty of using it with the leads pushed through a 2.5mm grid board is that the leads are on a 1.27mm spacing and often only 6.3mm long. No adapters exist for flat-pack use. One solution appears to be to bend the leads down at the spacings shown in Fig. 1(f) and drill holes in a blank board on a 1.27mm grid to match the resultant pattern.

When a printed circuit board is being laid out to receive microcircuits, the dressed lead spacings indicated above can be replicated exactly. With the TO-5, however, the designer often abandons the 2.5mm grid and merely symmetrically expands the pin circle diameter of the leads on the can (which is usually 5mm) to a diameter of 10mm on the board to give room for soldering pads round the holes.

Commercial microcircuits always have some index mark (e.g. the "pip" on a TO-5 can, or the coloured dot, or indent, on a flat-pack) to ensure that the device can be fitted in the right way round. The printing on the package is usually orientated in a fixed relation to the index mark, but sometimes you will find units with printing the wrong way round. Therefore, do not rely on the printing to orientate. Always look for the index mark, or you may have a 'dead' microcircuit in your hand.

Soldering

Microcircuit leads are generally designed to withstand temperatures of something like 325°C for ten seconds during soldering into circuit. Even so, always follow good soldering practice. Use a clean well-tinned iron, and heat the lead only long enough to ensure a good joint. Where the lead lengths permit, use one of the plastic pads available commercially for spacing the package off the board.

Use a miniature soldering bit, and do not apply the iron on a lead closer than 0.8mm to the body of the package. Many people grip the lead close to the body with a pair of fine-nosed pliers before soldering, to act as a 'heat shunt'.

The precautions detailed above of course would apply to soldering any very small component into circuit. But with microcircuits there is one special additional precaution necessary. The semiconductors in the microcircuit are prone to catastrophic failure if not protected from short high-voltage electrical "spikes". Remember that unearthed soldering irons are a fruitful source of these.

Some engineers find difficulty in unsoldering microcircuits, particularly those with many stout pin leads. Experienced bench hands use a large tinning iron (dressing the bit with a file into a suitable flat face), to melt the solder on all leads at the same time and swiftly withdraw the unit complete. In a production line special solder bits contoured to fit over all the leads at one time can be devised. Probably the most satisfactory way of unsoldering microcircuit leads is, however, to use one of the suction soldering irons now available. This neatly removes all the solder and permits clean easy withdrawal of the defective microcircuit.

Temperature

The soldering precautions discussed above are only one aspect of the thermal precautions to be taken with microcircuits. Generally, the cooler you keep a microcircuit, the longer it will live.

If there are any surfaces of the unit touching a larger mass (e.g. if the unit sits down on a printed circuit board) use silicone grease to mate the two touching faces for better heat removal. A variant of this is to use a thermally conductive epoxy such as Delta Cast 153 which has the additional advantage of holding the microcircuit firmly in position.

If you are mounting the microcircuit on a printed circuit board, leave as much copper on the board as possible to act as an extra radiator.

For supplementary heat removal use one of the 'add-on' heat sinks which are screwed or clipped onto the body of the microcircuit. Fig. 2 illustrates examples for use with multilead TO-5 cases. Inside equipment, always try to locate your

Common microcircuits tend to fall into two categories: industrial with maximum junction temperatures inside the package of about 150°C and entertainment with a maximum junction temperature of about 100°C. To get some idea of the permissible dissipation of the different packages, note that typically a multilead TO-5 has a thermal resistance from junction to ambient of around 150°C/W and from junction to case of around 45°C/W. By comparison, a dual-in-line is about 100°C/W junction-to-ambient and a flat-pack about 185°C/W junction-to-printed-circuit board.

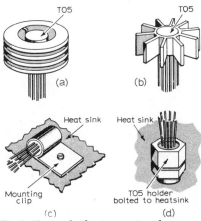

Fig. 2. Heatsinks for increasing the power dissipation of TO-5 microcircuits: (a) 'halo type', (b) 'corona type', (c) P-clip for attachment to a separate heatsink, (d) 'bolted-up' type for attachment to a separate heat sink.

microcircuit as far as practicable away from hot spots round mains transformers, rectifiers, etc. Study your data sheet thermal ratings and operate your microcircuit as far below the ratings as possible. Engineers looking for long trouble-free equipment life, aim to keep dissipation 25 to 50% down on the permissible maximum.

Power

Commercial single-polarity power supplies are often not ideal for working with microcircuits because many require a positive and a negative supply. Typical voltage requirements range from 15V to 5V, and currents up to about 150mA.

The relatively low currents and voltages required often lead experimenters to work with dry batteries. These are convenient and quite adequate, particularly if you use the grid-bias type with tappings at every 1.5V: A word of caution, however. If there is a danger of the microcircuit drawing damaging excess current from the supply, do not rely on the apparently limited current rating of the grid-bias battery. It may surprise you to discover that it can provide well over an amp for a few seconds, long enough to blow up an overloaded microcircuit.

Fig. 3 gives a circuit for a double power supply suitable for use with linear microcircuits with two convenient zener-stablished voltages, ±15V and ±5V.

Because of the dangers from fast voltage spikes, power supplies used with linear microcircuits should always be decoupled to r.f. by 0.1 to 0.01 μF ceramic (low-inductance) capacitors, these being in addition to any electrolytics used.

A danger with mains power supplies is that large smoothing capacitors can hold their voltages for a dangerously long time after switch off. Check that any supply used has some adequate 'bleeder' arrangement. In the version of Fig. 3, the pilot lamp circuit discharges the electrolytics rapidly on switch off.

overloads from external voltage transients. Firstly always operate well within the published ratings of the device. In the power supply, use a screened mains transformer with the screen adequately earthed.

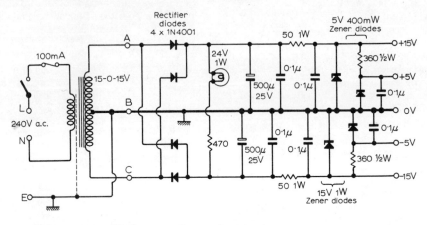

Fig. 3. Suitable power supply for most linear microcircuits.

With current-limited commercial power supplies, it might not seem important how the d.c. voltages vary on switch on and off, because the limited current available would not appear enough to damage the microcircuit. But such a supply may have sufficient output capacitance to provide a lethal spike for the microcircuit.

In work with microcircuits some engineers use an Avometer in series with the power supply and rely on the meter cut-out as a protection against damaging overloads. Apart from being bad for the Avometer, this puts inductance in the supply line which can easily lead to instability.

In working with mains power supplies on microcircuits, a cautious engineer will always turn off the supply before plugging in or unplugging the microcircuit.

Spikes

With microcircuits there are several steps you can take to guard against damaging

Always guard against reversed polarity in the power supply. Where you are trying different circuit arrangements on the bench, fit some form of diode protection against accidental reversal. A series diode connected as shown in Fig. 4(a) is a common precaution.

Where you install zeners to clip dangerous spikes, use fast devices such as the emitter-base junction of a silicon planar transistor rather than the slower alloy-construction zeners.

Use low-leakage silicon diodes as limiters at sensitive points in the circuit. Fig. 4 gives three examples. In Fig. 4(b) oppositely phased diodes across the inputs of a high-gain operational amplifier restrict to a safe limit the differential voltage that can be applied. In Fig. 4(c) zener diodes are used to limit the common mode input voltage. In Fig. 4(d) a diode in the feedback loop prevents input 'latch-up', i.e. the output overdriving the input so that the negative feedback becomes positive, and the amplifier saturates.

Always use test prods with special care around a microcircuit.

Design

Anyone used to working with transistors knows the increased dangers of instability

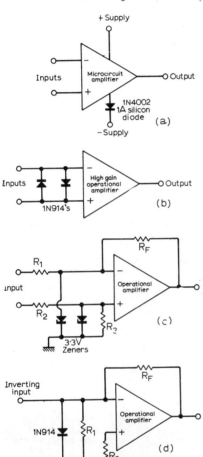

Fig. 4. How diodes can be used to protect op. amps from overloads. (a) preventing damage due to accidental power supply reversal, (b) limiting differential voltage inputs, (c) limiting common-mode voltage on the inputs, (d) protecting against latch-up.

that arose when they went over from the older germanium low-frequency alloy devices to typical planar silicon devices with frequency cut-off of hundreds of megahertz. Now in a microcircuit you may find crammed into a 1.27 × 1.27mm chip of silicon anything from five to fifteen such planar devices each capable of amplifying up to v.h.f.—an obvious invitation to r.f. instability and oscillation.

Additionally the circuit elements of the monolithic microcircuit are all connected through isolating reverse-biased diodes to the basic silicon substrate of the chip which has to be connected to the most negative point of the circuit supply. If instability arises or if supply polarities are accidentally reversed, these isolating diodes can become forward biased and allow damaging currents to flow.

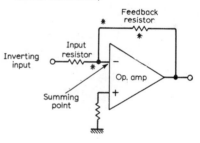

Fig.5. Points in an op. amp. feedback network which are very sensitive to electrical interference.

Always look upon a microcircuit as a high-gain v.h.f. amplifier. This means that you use an adequate single-point earth in your surrounding circuitry. Concentrate on the neatest layout possible. Use short supply leads. Also see that your supply leads (and particularly your earth leads) are of low inductance and resistance.

In your coupling and decoupling arrangements, recognize that aluminium electrolytics have a relatively high inductance. Where electrolytics are necessary, use tantalum types (which are low inductance and nowadays only a little more costly than aluminium). In general, connect a ceramic capacitor of about 0.1 μF in parallel with an electrolytic. By-pass r.f. to earth at both positive and negative supply rails. Look on every lead with jaundiced eye as an inductive choke

In shortening lead lengths, however, remember the dangers of uncontrolled feedback through interlead capacitances. In particular, always space your input lead as far as possible from the output and consider using shielded leads. With such high gain at v.h.f. you easily run the risk of r.f. interference, and you may on

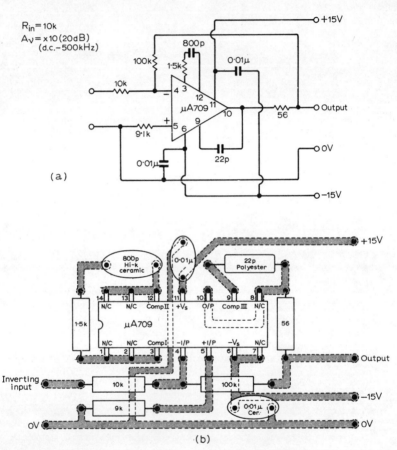

Fig. 6. (a) Circuit diagram of a 709 used as a $\times$ 10 (20dB) amplifier, (b) recommended layout.

and keep it as short as possible. Where you are operating more than one microcircuit from a supply, decouple each individually.

occasion have to go to the extreme of threading a ferrite bead on an input lead to avoid picking up your local taxi radio service!

As most general-purpose linear microcircuits are operational amplifiers, look carefully in your layout to the positioning of the summing point and the feedback resistor (indicated in Fig. 5) which are very sensitive to interference, and parasitics. If you want proof of this, just touch the feedback resistor and see what happens!

Fig. 6 shows a layout recommended for a standard μA 709 operational amplifier connected as a × 10 voltage amplifier taking into account the major precautions listed above.

Instability

High-gain linear microcircuit used at d.c. or low frequencies are prone to r.f. oscillation from 5 to 50 MHz. This oscillation can be 'Nyquist' (caused by incorrect design values of the intentional feedback loop components) or 'parasitic' (arising from unintended feedback through interlead capacitances, inadequately decoupled supplies, etc.).

'Motorboating'· (low-frequency oscillation) can also occur, but is usually easily cured by adequately large decoupling capacitors in the supply.

Curing Nyquist oscillations is mainly a matter of knowing basic feedback theory and studying the data sheet to see that the correct compensation network is used.

Parasitic oscillation is sometimes very difficult to eliminate because of the close proximity of the microcircuit leads. But good layout practice and adequate l.f.-cum-r.f. decoupling usually cures it.

Testing

There is no general-purpose instrument on the market for linear microcircuits. A single tester to deal with all the many different kinds of linear i.cs would be impossibly expensive. So, if you need a linear tester, you have to lash-up a separate circuit for each type you use.

As most linear microcircuits work on the principle of the op.amp however, a useful general-purpose piece of test gear is something to display the transfer function. Fig. 7(a) shows an arrangement for such a display. Fig. 7(b) shows the sort of trace to be expected, while Fig. 7(c) gives details of a circuit for the sawtooth generator to

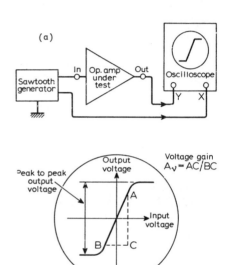

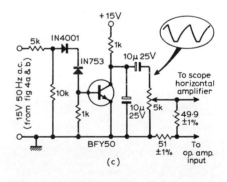

Fig. 7. Displaying the transfer characteristic of an op. amp. (a) general arrangement, (b) details of the oscilloscope display, (c) suggested circuit for the sawtooth generator part of (a).

provide drive voltages for the microcircuit input and the scope horizontal sweep input.

The oscilloscope finds another useful purpose in linear microcircuit work. Earlier we examined steps to avoid oscillation. The usual signs of oscillation are that the microcircuit is taking a heavy supply current or that the circuit operation is erratic. You can also detect oscillations on a scope, but as the oscillations can be occurring at up to 100 MHz, a low-frequency scope may only show you distortion or broadening of the l.f. trace. Because of the difficulties of getting a 'scope of sufficient bandwidth, use a small wideband r.f. detector or field-strength meter on the bench to detect oscillations.

CHAPTER 4

Three generations of operational amplifiers

Talk to the new breed of engineers practised in designing their circuits around readily available, economic, standard, monolithic operational amplifiers of the 1970s and you will find that for them op-amp is taking on a meaning different from the classical definition. Nowadays they think of it as a broadband, low-frequency, very-high-gain amplifier, for use from d.c. to about 1MHz in many circuit configurations.

If you look hard enough, you will find some 2,000 differently numbered operational amplifiers on the market. All but a few of these are of monolithic construction. The rest are specialist discrete-component or hybrid versions which designers turn to usually as a last resort when they cannot find the right monolithic.

First-generation

Until the appearance of monolithic op-amps in quantity in the late 1960s, a designer who needed such an amplifier would take conventional capacitors, resistors and transistors to make up a circuit something like Fig. 1. This employs a long-tail-pair balanced input followed by a long-tail-pair level shifter to return the single ended output to zero.

The first monolithic op-amp with a performance comparable to discrete-component versions was introduced in 1965. This was the Fairchild μA709. It is now available from most semiconductor manufacturers under many different code numbers, but it is always spoken of as the '709'. In the U.K. there are many variants such as Motorola's MC1709, Mullard/ Philips TAA521, National Semiconductors' LM709, Newmarket's LIC709, ITT's MIC709, Texas Instruments' SN72709 and Transitron's TOA2709, as well as Fairchild's own 709 series with code numbers such as U6A7709393.

Although the circuit of the 709, given in Fig. 2, achieved the same sort of performance as discrete circuits of the type of Fig. 1, it can be seen even under superficial inspection to be much more complex. This is because monolithic techniques for diffusing such an op-amp into a silicon chip (about 1.5 sq. mm) had difficulty in producing directly the high-value resistors and the high-gain transistors of the discrete version. For those interested in design details, a brief description follows.

In Fig. 2, the input transistors, Tr_1 and Tr_2 form a balanced long-tail pair with a fixed 40μA tail current provided by the transistor Tr_{11}. This is biased as a constant current source by the emitter resistor R_{11} and the diode-connected transistor Tr_{10} which is forward-biased by current through R_8, R_{10}. The collector load resistors of the long-tail pair, R_1, R_2, provide a balanced output.

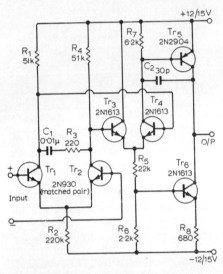

Fig. 1. Discrete component operational amplifier.

The network Tr_7, R_5, Tr_3, Tr_5, R_3, and Tr_{15} provide balanced stabilization against temperature and supply voltage changes. The single-ended output from R_2 drives the common-emitter Darlington pair, Tr_4, Tr_6, to give a further amplified signal level across R_6. This is used to drive Tr_8 which in turn (via the common-base stage Tr_9) controls the pre-output common emitter driver Tr_{12}. The collector of the driver (with its collector resistor R_{14}) is directly connected to the bases of the complementary-symmetry class-B output pair, Tr_{13}, Tr_{14}. The output is taken from the common emitters of Tr_{13}, Tr_{14}, the d.c. level having been shifted back to zero through transistors 4, 6, 8, 9, 12, 13 and 14.

In the discrete op-amp circuit of Fig. 1, capacitors C_1 and C_2 were included to cut the top frequency response of the circuit to avoid h.f. instability. In the 709 it was not possible to include capacitors and so terminals 1, 8 and 5 were provided to enable separate external compensation capacitors to be connected. The 220k Ω resistor R_2 in Fig. 1 also could not be provided in the monolithic version, and was replaced by the constant current transistor, Tr_{11}, in Fig. 2.

Selections of the 709 are available, but the loosest specification version (and the most commonly used), the 709C, has the following characteristics on $\pm$ 15V d.c. supply at 25°C ambient temperature:

A_{VOL} (open loop d.c. voltage gain)= 94dB ($\times$ 50,000) typ., 84dB min.

V_{IOS} (off-set voltage, 10k Ω source resistance)=2.0mV typ., 7.5mV max.

I_{IOS} (off-set current) 100nA typ., 500nA max.

I_B (input bias current)= 300nA typ. 1,500nA max.

R_{IN} (input resistance, differential)= 250k Ω typ., 50k min.

R_{OUT} (output resistance)= 150 Ω typ.

V_{OUT} (output voltage available swing) = $\pm$ 12V min. (R_L= 10k)
= $\pm$ 10V min. (R_L= 2K)

c.m.r.r. (common mode rejection ratio)= 90dB typ., 65dB min.

v.s.r.r. (supply voltage rejection ratio)= 25μV/V typ., 200μV/V max.

V_{in}*c.m.* (common mode input voltage range)= $\pm$ 10V typ., $\pm$ 8V max.

V_{in} *diff.* (differential input voltage range)= $\pm$ 5V max.

V_S (supply voltage range)= $\pm$ 9 to $\pm$ 15V.

SR (unity-gain slew rate)= 0.5V/μS typical.

BW_{OL} (open loop bandwidth)= 100Hz typ.

BW_{VF} (voltage follower or unity gain bandwidth)= 1MHz typ.

These characteristics are given in some detail so that you can see how far the first generation operational amplifiers matched up with the five ideal characteristics of an op-amp i.e. infinite gain, zero current and

min. was rather low. Without at least two external compensation capacitors it was virtually certain to oscillate on open loop. Its quiescent current consumption of about 2.5mA was too large.

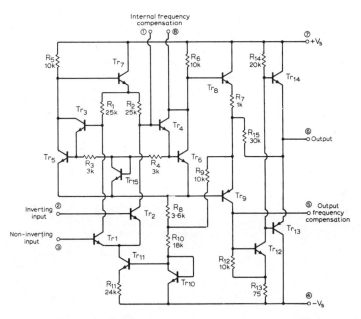

Fig. 2. The popular '709'.

voltage input offset, infinite input impedance, zero output impedance and zero response time (infinite bandwidth). They also set levels to judge how later generation op-amps improved.

Improved first-generation
Users found that the 709 had certain practical drawbacks. In ordinary use it was liable to latch up when the common mode input range of ±8V was exceeded. It was liable to 'blow up' if the output was short circuited. Its input resistance of 50kΩ

The first improvement of the 709 was the LM101 brought out in 1967 by National Semiconductors with the circuit of Fig. 3. It is now almost as well known as the 709 and commonly referred to as the '101'.

The principal improvements incorporated in the 101 were frequency compensation by a single 30pF external capacitor, voltage supply range extended to ±5 to ±20V, quiescent current reduced to 1.8mA typical, continuous output short-circuit protection provided, common mode input voltage limit raised to ±15V, and differential input voltage range raised to ±30V. Also a

27

separate terminal was used for easy offset zeroing (balancing) with a single 5MΩ potentiometer.

These improvements were substantial, but the 101 is usually regarded merely as a slightly better 709, because the offset

In the case of the LH101, the modification to the LM101 was merely to diffuse a 30pF capacitor internally between the compensation and top balance terminals of Fig. 3.

In the case of the 741, a completely new

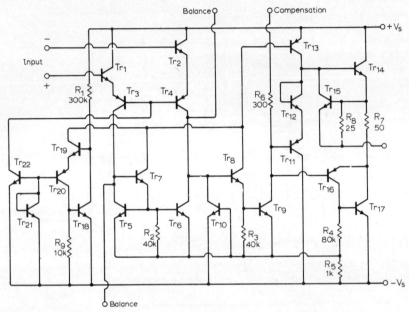

Fig. 3. An example of an improved first generation op-amp, the LM101.

voltage and offset currents were only marginally improved. The Fairchild μA748 has very similar specifications. The Motorola MC1533 is another well known improved 709.

First generation internally-compensated

The 101 still could not be used open-loop without an external compensating capacitor, and almost inevitably in 1968 there came out the first fully internally compensated op-amp, the μA741. This was followed soon by the LH101, or RM4101, (compensated 101).

circuit as Fig. 4 was used. In this the high-gain n-p-n transistors Tr_1, Tr_2 are used in combination with the low-gain lateral p-n-p transistors Tr_3, Tr_4 to provide effectively a high-gain p-n-p input pair. Transistors Tr_8 and Tr_9 provide a constant-current long-tail source of about 30μA total for this input pair. Transistors Tr_5 and Tr_6 are biased to act as 2MΩ loads for the composite input transistors. The amplified signal appearing at the collector of Tr_4 is further amplified by the high-input-impedance Darlington pair Tr_{16}, Tr_{17}. The collector load of this Darlington is the collector output resistance of the constant-current-biased transistor Tr_{13}.

28

This drives the output complementary-symmetry, transistors Tr_{14}, Tr_{20} which are biased class AB to about $60\mu A$ quiescent current by the forward voltage drop across Tr_{18}. The forward bias on the output transistors eliminates the cross-over distortion of the 709 (where the bases of the output transistors are connected together —see Fig. 2).

The 741 is proof against continuous output short-circuits because the output is current limited. For positive excursions R_9, Tr_{15} in Fig. 4 act as a 25mA current limiter.

30pF m.o.s. capacitor (C in Fig 4). As a result the amplifier does not need any external frequency compensation, even for closed loop gains down to unity.

It has an internal 6dB/octave roll-off commencing at 10Hz, passing through unity gain at 800kHz, to ensure a typical 80° phase margin at unity gain.

The high emitter-base breakdown voltages of the lateral p-n-p transistors Tr_3, Tr_4 means that the 741 circuit is able to withstand $\pm30V$ differential input signals without breakdown (compared with the $\pm5V$ max of the 709).

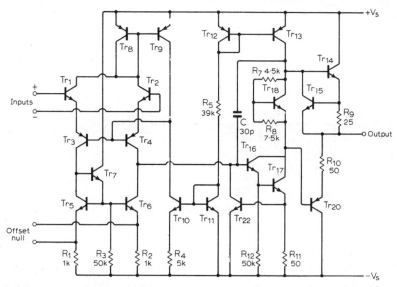

Fig. 4. The μA741. Note the diffused compensation capacitor.

Above this output current, the voltage drop across R_9 brings Tr_{15} into conduction and limits the drive. For negative excursions the output current is limited by the 50-Ω series resistor R_{10} combined with the transistor Tr_{22} shunted across the drive. On the negative excursion the current through R_{11} tends to turn Tr_{22} on and limit the drive to the output.

The completely new feature of the 741 op-amp was that the chip incorporates a

The process improvements of the 741 did not make much overall improvement in the characteristics of the 709 (except for slightly increased gain and higher input resistance). Improvements were rather that the 741 had protection against output short circuit damage and input latch up, a larger differential voltage range, internal frequency compensation, simple offset voltage nulling with a single 10kΩ potentiometer (connected across emitters of Tr_5, Tr_6,

29

in Fig. 4), wider operating voltage range (±3 to ±20V) and lower quiescent supply current (1.7 as against 2.5mA typical).

The 741 appears under various numbers such as Motorola's MC1741, National Semiconductors' LM741, Newmarket's LIC741, Transitron's TOA2741, ITTs MIC 741 and Texas Instrument's SN72741.

As a parallel development, we find manufacturers providing two op-amps in one package with the useful characteristic of close thermal tracking between the chips. Well known examples of dual 709s are the

hundreds of nanoamps which led to unacceptable voltage drifts with temperature in high-impedance circuits.

The second generation of monolithic op-amps was characterized by an order of magnitude improvement in bias and offset currents. The National Semiconductor's LM101A was the archetype of these. It has 20nA max. offset current compared with the 500nA limit of the 709 and its previous successors. Similarly in the 101A the input bias current was improved from 1.5μA to 0.25μA max.

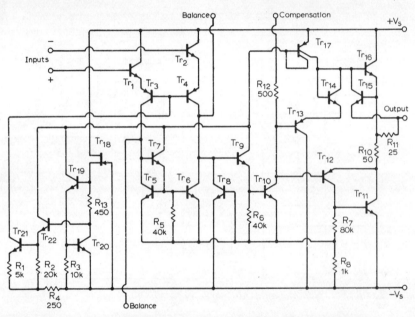

Fig. 5. Second generation example, the LM101A. Both bipolar and field effect transistors are used.

Transitron TOA2809, and Motorola MC1437, and of dual 741s the TOA2841 and MC1558.

Second generation
All the op-amps discussed so far have input offset and bias currents measured in

The circuit of the LM101A, given in Fig. 5, has several interesting features, making extensive use of transistors and f.e.ts as active collector loads, high-gain lateral p-n-p transistors and pinch resistors.

The circuit of the 101A in Fig. 5 can be traced by noting that Tr_5 and Tr_6 act as active collector loads for

30

the balanced input stage Tr_1/Tr_3, Tr_2/Tr_4. The right hand transistor Tr_4 drives the common-emitter Darlington pair Tr_9, Tr_{10}, whose collector load is Tr_{17} (via Tr_{13}, Tr_{14}). The drives to the bases of the output transistors Tr_{16}, and Tr_{11} are from Tr_{17} collector and from Tr_{10} collector via Tr_{12}.

The active collector loads Tr_5, Tr_6 are better than resistor loads. They avoid the use of large resistances to achieve low current operation (important in reducing input bias currents and power consumption). They do not require much voltage to be dropped across them for correct operation, which leads to an increase in common-mode input range, an increase in voltage swing, a wider permissible range of supply voltages, and higher stage gains (lessening the number of stages required and simplifying frequency compensation).

Transistor Tr_{18} in Fig. 5 is an example of an f.e.t. used as an active constant-current-source collector load for transistor Tr_{20}.

Lateral p-n-p transistors first featured in the 709 (Tr_9 in Fig. 2) were originally very low-gain devices (with current gains much less than 10) and low frequency cut-offs (typically about 1MHz). By the time the 101A was brought out in late 1968, processes had improved so much that lateral p-n-p current gains of greater than 100 were achieved. Tr_3 and Tr_4 in Fig. 5 are examples of such later transistors. A further development of the lateral p-n-p is the 'controlled gain' transistor in which the collector is split into two segments and one of them is connected back to the base. The effective current gain is determined by the relative areas of the two collector segments. Tr_{17} in Fig. 5 is such a controlled-gain transistor.

'Pinch' or 'pinched-base' resistors are special high-value diffused resistors originally developed to get round the fact that conventional base-diffused resistors of values above a few thousand ohms were impracticable. The cross sectional area of a base-diffused resistor is effectively reduced or 'pinched' by an emitter-diffusion on top of it. By this process resistor values up to 100kΩ are feasible. R_2, R_5, R_6 and R_7 in Fig. 5 are examples of such high-value 'pinch' resistors.

Further examples of other op-amps of this lower input current second generation are the well-known Motorola MC1539/1439 and the Sprague 2139.

Third Generation

The second generation 101A had given input bias and offset currents of 250nA and 20nA max. compared with 1,500 and 500nA in the first generation 709. By 1970, monolithic bipolar technology had enabled a further order of magnitude reduction in input currents in the 'third generation' op-amps. In them the National Semiconductors LM108 led the way. In this, input bias and offset currents dropped to 2nA and 0.2nA max.

This improvement is achieved by using 'super-gain' or 'punch-through' transistor at the input. The current gain of an n-p-n transistor in a monolith depends for one thing on the length of the emitter diffusion cycle in the manufacture. Devices emitter diffused for unusually long time exhibit increased current gain at the expense of collector breakdown voltage. Current gains of 4,000 can be obtained but with a collector breakdown voltage of 4V.

In Fig. 6, the circuit of the LM108, low-voltage super-gain transistors are used as Tr_1, Tr_2, the input transistors. To prevent voltage breakdown they are operated in cascode connection with Tr_5 and Tr_6, which stand off the common-mode voltage. The bases of Tr_5 and Tr_6 are bootstrapped via Tr_{27} and Tr_{28} to the common-mode voltage seen by the input transistors. Thus the input transistors are always operated with near-zero collector-base voltage, and high temperature leakage currents do not show up at the input.

The super-gain input transistors give other bonuses. The 108 input resistance is 30 MΩ min. compared with the 50kΩ min.

31

of the 709. Voltage gain improves to 94dB min. instead of 84dB. Common mode rejection ratio becomes 80dB min. instead of 65dB. Typical supply current drops from 2.5mA to 0.15mA.

At first sight a Darlington compound should give the same sort of result as a super gain device. However the Darlington pair voltage mismatch tends to be worse because it depends on current gains; also

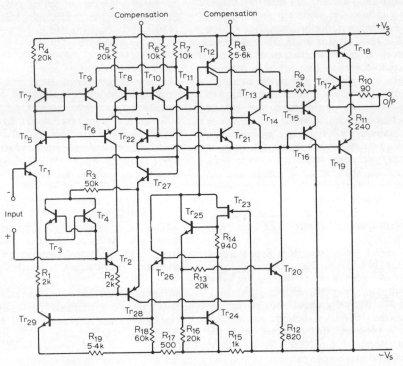

Fig. 6. Third generation example, the LM108. Tr_1 and Tr_2 are 'super-gain' or 'punch-through' transistors which operate at very low voltages.

The Motorola MC1556 is another third generation op-amp. using super-gain input transistors, and you will also find similar transistors incorporated in the unity gain, voltage-followers LM102 and LM110.

High input impedance
The low input resistance of the 709 led to the development of special high R_{IN} monolithics along two lines—Darlington pairs and f.e.ts for the inputs.

it tends to be higher noise and exhibits lower common mode rejection. The Transitron TOA8709 is a well known example of such a Darlington input.

The f.e.t. input transistor approach is used in the Fairchild μA740 where an input resistance of $10^{12}\,\Omega$ is achieved with a typical offset current of only 20pA. Against this, f.e.t.—input op-amps exhibit offset voltages and voltage drifts about twenty times higher than the typical 1mV and 2μV/°C of the super-gain transistor approach. (Even lower bias and offset currents have been obtained by hybrid assembly using selected matched f.e.t. chips at the input as in the Teledyne AD503.)

Higher slew-rate

One of the defects of earlier generation op-amps was the limited small signal and power bandwidths, usually specified by unity gain bandwidth (for small signal) and unity gain slew rate for full output. The 709 had a 1MHz typical bandwidth and $0.5V/\mu s$ slew rate, the major restriction being the low gain, low frequency lateral p-n-p used (Tr_9 in Fig. 2). Process improvements in later generation general-purpose op-amps pushed gain-bandwidths out to about 5MHz and slew rate to about $5V/\mu s$.

However for higher slew rate requirements, special op-amps have been developed such as the Signetic 531 (typical $40V/\mu s$) or the Optical Electronics 9694 ($100V/\mu s$).

Micropower

Another area where specialist op-amps have been developed is low power consumption. In this area, the Solitron UC4250 indicates the sort of performance aimed at.

This micropower op-amp uses so little power that its batteries last as long as their shelf life. It can operate on rails from $\pm 1V$ to $\pm 18V$. It has typical input bias currents of only 3nA and zero input offset temperature drift. On $\pm 1V$ it has a power consumption of only $20\mu W$.

Conclusion

The second half of the 1960s was an astonishing time when the monolithic op-amp developed from the old-faithful 709 (which in the 1970's still does over half the op-amp. jobs around) through the 101A up to the 108. We now have a situation where the handy monolith is bidding fair to oust all discrete or hybrids of the balanced differential input type, is giving a performance near to chopper stabilized types, and could well in time even match the heights of the varactor-bridge and electrometer valve.

33

CHAPTER 5

Everyday uses of monolithic operational amplifiers

It should be realised by this time that a monolithic op-amp is really a 'gain block' of electronic amplification that, because of its low cost, is set fair to displace discrete transistors far outside the analogue computer field for which it was originally designed.

We will pass over the use of op-amps for the mathematical operations of addition, subtraction, integration, differentiation, level sensing, etc. that form the basis of analogue computers and instead we will take a look at how designers are using them in more mundane circuits.

D.C. amplifiers

Although most run-of-the-mill circuits tend to be a.c., we will start with d.c. amplifiers, because much d.c. circuitry carries over readily from analogue computers.

Most op-amps have two inputs and at least one output. This is shown in diagrams by the symbol for an op-amp (a triangle on its side) having ' − ' and ' + ' inputs on the left and an output on the right (as in Fig.1). The + input signal appears amplified at the output without phase inversion, and this input is therefore

known as a 'non-inverting' input. A signal applied to the − input is amplified to the same extent as a signal at the + input, but appears at the output 180° out of phase with the input. Therefore the − input is known as the 'inverting' input.

You will find in Fig.1(a) the basic 'resistance ratio' inverted configuration of the op-amp. In this the voltage gain is the ratio of the feedback resistance R_2 to the input resistance R_1. The op-amp input terminals are at virtual earth. This means that the input resistance of the inverted circuit is equal to the series resistance R_1. This fact can lead to complications where you want high input resistance combined with high gain. If R_1 is large, then for a high gain, A_v, the feedback resistance = $A_v \times R_1$ can become impracticably large. Designers can then adopt the modified circuit of Fig.1 (b). In this, high gain can be achieved along with high input resistance. It uses a lower value of R_2 to get part of the required total gain. The rest arises from the potentiometer, R_4, R_3 across the output, which reduces the proportion of the output fed back into the feedback network.

The resistance-ratio inverted configuration gives a very tightly controlled fixed gain. However, many circuits call for adjustable gain, and Figs. 1(c) to (f) show arrangements that can be adopted for variable gain with an inverted op-amp.

In Fig.1(c) the feedback resistance R_2 of Fig.1(a) is replaced by a variable resistance R_v. This has the advantage that the input resistance is not affected by the gain setting, but also the disadvantage that the variable resistance is very sensitive to hum and noise pick-up.

Fig.1(d) shows an arrangement used to give more flexible gain variation. Here the feedback and input resi nces are combined in one potentiometer, and the setting of the potentiometer slider adjusts the gain. With an ideal op-amp the gain could be varied in this way from zero to infinity, but of course this is not possible in practice. Fig.1(d) has the defect that the input resistance of the circuit varies widely with the setting of the gain control. Also the rate of control is highly non-linear.

Fig.1(e) is another variant sometimes found in which the feedback resistor is kept constant and only the input resistance R_v varied. Here the gain is inversely proportional to the resistance of the variable resistance and the circuit input resistance varies with the gain setting.

A final variable-gain circuit in which the feedback and input resistors are not altered is given in Fig.1(f). Here, the gain

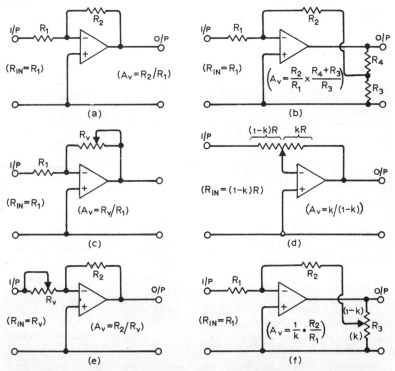

Fig. 1. The op-amp 'inverted' configuration; (a) 'standard' fixed gain arrangement; (b) modification for high gain without unduly low input resistance; (c) gain control by varying feedback resistance only; (d) varying feedback and input resistance together; (e) varying input resistance only; (f) varying proportion of output applied to feedback network.

is set by a potentiometer across the output which varies the proportion of the output allowed into the feedback network. It has the big advantage that the variable element is across the output (a low impedance part of the circuit), and is buffered by the feedback resistor from the input virtual earths which are very sensitive to noise and pick-up.

Fig.2(a) shows the standard fixed gain resistance-ratio non-inverted configuration for the monolithic op-amp. This

Gain variation in the non-inverted configuration can be achieved in a number of ways. Fig.2(b) shows the 'top' feedback resistor being varied. Fig.2(c) shows both the feedback and 'fedback' resistors being varied. Fig.2(d) achieves gain control by varying only the 'fedback' resistor. Each arrangement has its own advantages and disadvantages. The formulae for input resistance and voltage gain appropriate to each arrangement are noted on the circuit diagram. Inspection of these will show

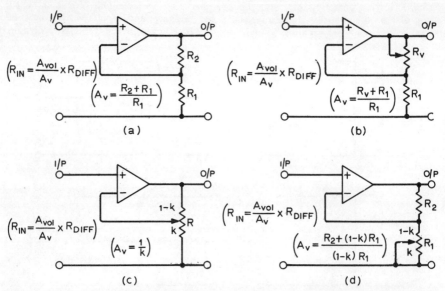

Fig. 2. The op-amp 'non-inverted' configuration; (a) fixed gain 'standard' arrangement; (b) gain control by varying output feedback resistance only; (c) varying feedback and 'fedback' resistance together; (d) varying 'fedback' resistance only.

arrangement has the big advantage compared with the inverted configuration that the input resistance is high, being roughly equal to the op-amp's differential input resistance multiplied by the 'loop gain'. Loop gain being the ratio of the op-amp's intrinsic (open loop) gain to the gain with feedback. This configuration is therefore widely used when high input impedance is important.

which element it is best to vary for your particular problem.

In order to measure accurately d.c. voltages much below 1V where ordinary meters run out, the inverting configuration of an op-amp is widely used. Provided the voltage being measured has a low source impedance, a resistance ratio of up to 100:1 can be used to bring the measured voltage up to the level at which it can be read

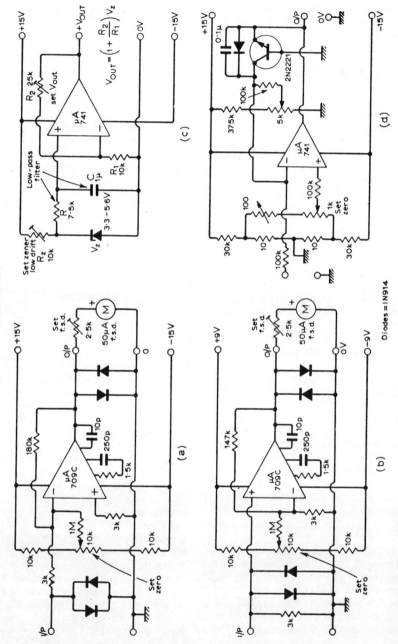

Fig. 3. Some useful op-amp d.c. circuits; (a) amplifier to give 2.5mV d.c. full scale on 50μA range of an Avometer; (b) amplifier for 1μA d.c. full scale with Avometer; (c) adjustable zener reference voltage; (d) logarithmic amplifier.

37

accurately on a meter. Fig.3(a) gives a typical practical circuit for measuring 2.5mV d.c. full scale on the 50μ. A range of an Avometer.

The monolithic op-amp also proves very valuable for measuring low d.c. currents. When it is necessary to measure currents substantially less than the 50μ. A full-scale of readily available meters, the current can be fed through a small resistor and the resulting d.c. voltage drop measured. Fig.3(b) is just such a practical circuit for measuring 1μ A d.c. full scale with a 50μ meter.

The monolithic op-amp can readily provide a constant-voltage reference source. Typical of such applications is the circuit of Fig.3(c) which permits the precise voltage from a zener diode to be adjusted upwards to some other precise voltage.

When you have played around with op-amps for a while, you will discover many useful d.c. circuits. They are, for example, peculiarly suited to such arrangements as the logarithmic amplifier shown in Fig.3(d). This has the property of rapid variation around zero and logarithmic fall off in gain for higher signal levels. This makes it most useful as a null detector.

Most of the circuitry discussed above is expressed in terms of neat little op-amps with only two input terminals and an output-terminal. Real op-amps have other characteristics needing more components which make practical circuitry much less simple looking.

Firstly it should not be overlooked that the op-amp is not merely a d.c. amplifier but a d.c. to 1MHz amplifier. For d.c. use it is essential that compensation of some sort is applied in the circuit to prevent oscillation. It is impossible to give any simple rules of thumb on applying compensation networks to commercial op-amps because they often have different compensation terminals and networks. Get hold of the data sheet for the device you propose to use. Study it with care and

follow closely the recommendations of the manufacturers on the C and R networks to be connected to the various terminals to prevent instability.

The other thing that is missing in most diagrams discussing op-amp uses is any indication of the d.c. power supply. In d.c. use, the op-amp must have both positive and negative supply rails, because of its 'd.c. integrity' (i.e. its output being at zero when its input is at zero). However, provided the precautions on adequate h.f. and l.f. decoupling on the supply rails discussed in earlier chapters are followed, little difficulty will be met with in practice on this double supply requirement. Because it is so often overlooked, however, it might pay to look more closely at the question of providing supply rails which are positive and negative with reference to a signal earth.

D.C. supply for op-amps

In op-amp basic theory, two independent power supplies to give positive and negative rails are tacitly assumed as in Fig.4(a) and (b) for inverted and non-inverted configurations. The V_{CC} and V_{EE} batteries in Figs.4(a) and (b) could equally well be centre-tapped positive and negative mains powered d.c. supplies.

In working with op-amps many circuit men want to use a single power supply, and find some difficulty in adapting the single supply to perform the function of the double supply.

Note that in diagrams Figs.1(a) and (b) both inputs of the op-amp have a continuous d.c. path to the centre rail or signal earth. With the single power supply, a centre-rail signal earth can be achieved by a bleeder resistance network R_1, R_2 across the power supply as in Fig. 4(c). In practice R_1 and R_2 are usually made equal. Also the values are chosen to give a bleeder current at least ten times the peak output current into the load resistance from the op-amp. This is necessary because the bleeder resistances are in series with the load resistance and must be low enough in value not to reduce excessively the peak voltage swing across the load resistance.

For a 5mA peak current in the load the above rule for the bleeder network would mean a standing current of 50mA, and this might be unacceptable. An alternative is then to set up the centre rail with two zener diodes as in Fig. 4(d). Because of the low dynamic resistance of the Zener diodes, the standing current in the bleeder

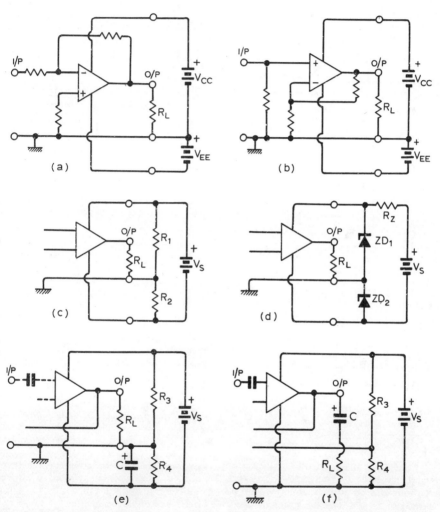

Fig. 4. Supply arrangements for monolithic op-amps; (a) 'inverted' configuration double (±) supply; (b) non-inverted double supply; (c) bleeder resistance-split single supply; (d) zener-split single supply; (e) resistance-split supply for a.c. use with signal earth to centre rail; (f) resistance-split supply for a.c. use with signal earth to negative supply rail.

network need be only slightly larger than the peak current into the load (for a μA709 some 8mA).

So far, we have been considering single power supply arrangements for d.c. operation of op-amps. For a.c. operation, the bleeder current demands can be much less.

few tens or hundreds of microamps. The resultant large values of R_3 and R_4, being effectively in series with the load resistor R_L, would seriously limit the output drive under a.c. conditions were it not for the large decoupling capacitor, C, across R_4 from the centre rail to the negative of the power supply. The time constant CR_4 is

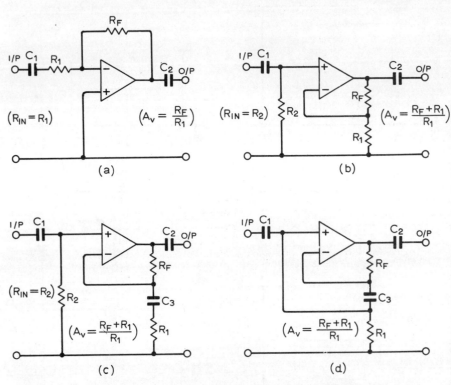

Fig. 5. Arrangements for a.c. amplifiers using basic op-amps; (a) inverted; (b) non-inverted; (c) non-inverted with 100% d.c. negative feedback; (d) high input impedance 'non-inverted'.

Fig.4(e) shows an a.c. amplifier resistance bleeder arrangement. Resistors R_3 and R_4 need be only small enough to provide a current which is large compared with the bias leakage currents at the op-amp inputs (which are usually, at most, only a few microamps). This means that the current through R_3, R_4 need be only a

chosen so that the bleeder network presents negligible impedance compared with the load resistance at the lowest frequency of a.c. operation.

The same low bleeder current can be used for a.c. applications in the arrangement of Fig.4(f). Here the input signal is applied between the op-amp input and the negative of the power supply. The load resistance is also connected via an isolating capacitor from the op-amp output to the negative of the power supply.

A.C. op-amp circuits

Although op-amps are essentially d.c. amplifiers, they are more and more being used by circuit engineers for a.c. applications.

The basic inverted configuration discussed earlier as Fig.1(a) can be simply converted to a.c. use as in Fig.5(a) by isolating capacitors C_1 and C_2 at input and output. The non-inverted configuration of Fig.1(b) can be similarly converted to a.c. use as in Fig.5(b).

Both Figs.5(a) and 5(b) have the disadvantage that the d.c. off-set voltages are amplified equally with the a.c. voltages with consequent dangers of excessive d.c. output voltage drift. The arrangement of Fig.5(c), with virtually 100% d.c. feedback, amplifies only the a.c. voltage so that no substantial d.c. off-set occurs at the output. Here the mid-band a.c. gain of the circuit is $(R_F + R_1)/R_1$.

Where a higher a.c. input impedance is required, the bootstrap circuit of Fig.5(d) is useful.

Frequency response tailoring

Thus far we have considered only the mid-band gain of a.c.-coupled op-amps. Apart from the use of the input and output capacitors to tailor low-frequency response, the wealth of resistors in the various feedback networks make a happy hunting ground for frequency response tailoring.

In the basic inverted configuration of Fig.6(a) R_3 and C_3 across the input resistance R_1 will boost top frequencies, while C_4, R_4 across the feedback resistance will cut them.

Similarly in the non-inverted configurations of Fig.6(b), C_4, R_4 across the input bias resistance, and C_5, R_5 across the

feedback resistance R_F both act as top cut networks. C_6, R_6 across the lower resistor R_1 of the feedback network serve to cut bass frequencies, as does C_3 in series with R_1.

To illustrate frequency tailoring by these methods some practical circuits are given. Fig.6(c) is a 'flat' microphone amplifier with a 20 to 20,000 Hz response. Fig.6(d) is a tape replay amplifier where the networks provide the 17dB bass boost required. Fig.6(e) shows a pre-amplifier with the compensation necessary for a magnetic pickup. Finally Fig.6(f) shows a high-input-impedance circuit for use with a crystal pickup.

Frequency tailoring so far shown is confined to attenuating low and high frequencies. But, by incorporating frequency selective networks (such as the twin-T or Wein bridge) in the feedback network, there is great scope for making op-amps into band-pass and band-reject amplifiers with ease.

Special op-amp circuits

Apart from 'simple' d.c. and a.c. amplifiers, op-amps have now become widely used for general circuit purposes. In an article of this length it is impossible to examine all the uses made of them, but the selection given in Fig.7 gives some indication of the scope.

An audio mixer can be made up with the arrangement of Fig.7(a). This is an adaptation of the 'adder' circuit of the analogue computer.

The circuit of Fig.7(b) gives you a simple slow-speed bistable flip-flop which can be triggered to either positive or negative rail saturation at the output. For a monostable flip-flop, the arrangement of Fig.7(c) can be used. The length of time the monostable is 'on' can be controlled by a d.c. voltage applied to the non-inverting (+) terminal. In Fig.4(d) an op-amp is used to provide an astable flip-flop with a symmetrical square wave output.

To overcome the non-linearity of the

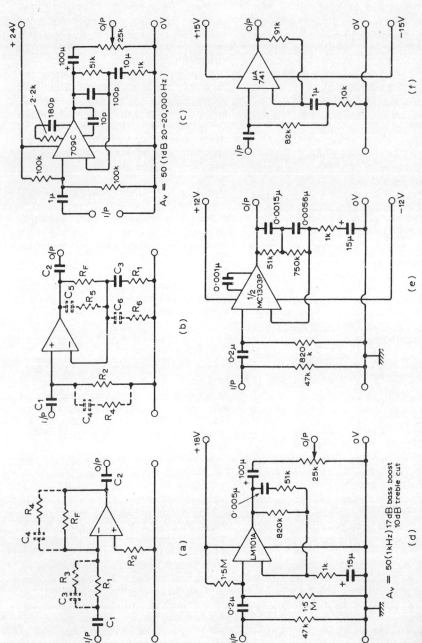

Fig. 6. Frequency response tailoring of op-amp amplifiers: (a) inverted configuration paths for incorporating frequency dependent networks; (b) non-inverted configuration frequency tailoring; (c) flat (microphone) pre-amp with bottom and top roll off; (d) tape replay pre-amplifier with bass boost; (e) magnetic pick-up pre-amp; (f) crystal pick-up pre-amp.

42

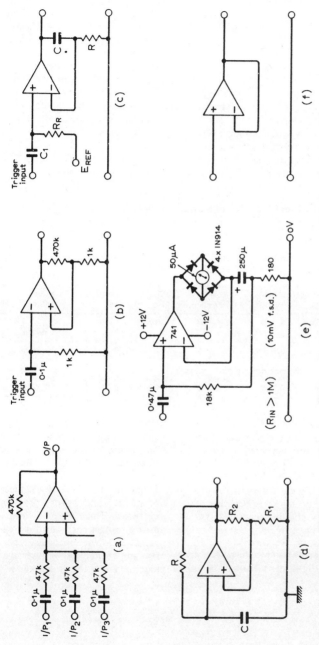

Fig. 7. Special op-amp a.c. circuits; (a) audio mixer; (b) bistable multivibrator; (c) monostable flip flop; (d) a stable multivibrator (symmetrical square wave); (e) linear a.c. millivoltmeter; (f) voltage follower (high to low impedance).

43

diodes used in meter rectification of a.c. signals, a very linear a.c. milivoltmeter circuit can be made up with an op-amp as shown in Fig.7(e). The circuit values given provide 10mV full-scale deflection when used with a 50μ A d.c. meter.

Finally a common requirement in circuit design is a voltage follower circuit which gives an output voltage equal to the input voltage but has a high input impedance and a low output impedance, i.e. an impedance conversion circuit. The op-amp can be connected as shown in Fig.7(f) to provide this facility.

resistance ratio formula and having little practical bench experience. Other circuits call for a fair knowledge of frequency compensation techniques, and a good working experience with practical circuits. Some again call for considerable practical bench experience and theoretical knowledge. And finally some circuit areas are pushing the limits of currently available op-amps even for the most knowledgeable, skilled and highly experienced.

To give some guidance on where, as Table 1 sets out types of circuit in degrees

Table 1 Design difficulties with operational amplifiers

Skill required	Circuit type						
	Signal frequency	Signal voltage	Signal current	Circuit impedance	Accuracy	Slew-rate (unity gain. large signal)	Full power band-width
little	d.c.—100kHz	above 100mV	above 100nA	below 1MΩ	worse than 1%.	below 1V/μs	below 10kHz
fair	100kHz—1MHz	3–100mV	3–100nA	1–30MΩ	0.1–1%	1–10V/μs	10–100kHz
high	1–100MHz	0.1–3mV	0.1–3nA	30–1000MΩ	0.01–0.1%	10–100V/μs	100kHz–1MHz
exceptional	above 100MHz	below 0.1mV	below 0.1nA	above 1000 MΩ	better than 0.01%	above 100V/μs	above 1MHz

Common sense precautions

The various circuits set out above give an indication of the multiple uses to which op-amps can be put. However, it is well not to be deceived by the apparent simplicity of the circuit diagrams. Many precautions must be taken in practice to prevent instability and unacceptable d.c. drift.

The efficient use of op-amps depends to a great extent on skill. Some circuits can be made up knowing little more than the gain

of difficulty, in terms of signal frequency, signal voltage, signal current circuit impedances, accuracy, slew rate and full-power bandwidth. In each of these areas it offers suggested limits to work to, dependent on your mathematics, your knowledge and your practical bench experience. There may be some argument among engineers about the exact crossover points between the different areas but the table should serve as a useful guide to tyro in the op-amp art.

CHAPTER 6

Audio amplifiers

If you need an audio amplifier you could design a circuit yourself using discrete transistors. Alternatively you might use a standard off-the-shelf 'packaged circuit' (i.e. amplifiers already assembled on printed circuit boards). But nowadays you are most likely to turn to one of the commercially available integrated circuits.

In the i.c. field most of the linear amplifier circuits available that could be used for audio requirements are general purpose op-amps. To get the gain and frequency response needed for this type of op-amp you have to connect it into a network of resistors and capacitors (as discussed in previous articles in this series).

However, i.c. manufacturers have recognized that some people may not want to play about with discrete components and they have come up in recent years with 'special function' audio amplifiers.

These incorporate in the package as many as possible of the passive components that would normally have to be used externally with a general purpose op-amp. Thus there has grown up the breed of audio amplifier integrated circuits discussed in this article.

As yet, specific audio amplifiers form only a small part of the total linear amplifier microcircuits on the market. A count at the beginning of 1971 showed about 150

a.f. amplifier types against about 1500 general purpose op-amps. Another interesting feature that emerged from the count was that while the U.S.A. was the leader in general purpose op-amps., Western Europe appears to have established a powerful position out in front in monolithic a.f. amplifiers and Japan in hybrid.

Commercially available audio amplifier microcircuits fall readily into three categories, (1) pre-amplifiers (low level up to 50mW output); (2) amplifiers (mid-level with from 50 to 500mW output); and (3) power amplifiers (high level from 0.5W output upwards).

Because of the power dissipation handling difficulties in a very small chip, monolithic integrated circuits tend to be limited to pre-amplifiers and amplifiers. Power amplifiers (and certainly high-power amplifiers above about 5W) are usually thick film hybrid assemblies.

As yet there is no standardization of integrated circuit audio amplifiers. Each company engaged in their manufacture has its own special versions. In addition, while the market is settling down to some standardization, companies may produce models which subsequently go off the market or are superseded by new versions (as, for example, the PA122 of G.E., U.S.A., now superseded by the PA234).

In the circuits given later in this chapter it will be seen as yet little in common between the different manufacturers except that most use class A at low level and class AB complementary push-pull at high levels. So far, little use has been made of class D, although it has many features that suits it to monolithic or hybrid integration.

Table 1 lists audio amplifier microcircuits fairly readily available in the U.K. The list is still a short one, but over the next few years it will lengthen appreciably.

TABLE 1
Microcircuit directory—a.f. amplifiers

CA3007	RCA	A.	100mW
CA3020	RCA	A.	500mW
CA3048	RCA	P.	(×4),*12V
CA3052	RCA	P.	(×4), 16V
MC1302	Motorola	P.	(×2), 12V
MC1303	Motorola	P.	(×2), 26V
MC1306	Motorola	A.	200mW
MC1454	Motorola	A.	1W
MC1554	Motorola	A.	1W
MFC4000P	Motorola	A.	
MFC8010P	Motorola	A.	1W
MFC8040P	Motorola	P.	
MFC9000P	Motorola	A.	4W
MFC9010P	Motorola	A.	2W
OM200	Philips	P.	1.3V
PA222	GE (U.S.A.)	A.	1W
PA230	GE (U.S.A.)	P.	12V
PA234	GE (U.S.A.)	A.	1W
PA237	GE (U.S.A.)	A.	2W
PA239	GE (U.S.A.)	P.	(×2) 24V
PA246	GE (U.S.A.)	A.	5W
PA263	GE (U.S.A.)	A.	3.5W
SI-1020A	Sanken	A.	25W
SI-1050A	Sanken	A.	50W
SL402A	Plessey	A.	1.5W
SL403A	Plessey	A.	2.5W
SL630C	Plessey	P.	12V
TAA103	Philips	P.	6V
TAA111	Siemens	P.	4.5V
TAA121	Siemens	P.	4.5V
TAA141	Siemens	P.	3V
TAA151	Siemens	P.	7V
TAA1515	Siemens	P.	12V
TAA263	Philips	P.	6V
TAA293	Philips	P.	6V
TAA300	Philips	A.	1W
TAA310	Philips	P.	7V
TAA320	Philips	P.	m.o.s.t.
TAA370	Philips	P.	1.3V
TAA420	Siemens	P.	7.5V
TAA435	Philips	D.	14V
TAA480	Philips	P.	7V
TH9013P	Toshiba	A.	20W
μA716	Fairchild	P.	21V
μA745	Fairchild	P.	6.3V

P—pre-amplifier;   A—power amplifier;

D—driver amplifier.

*× followed by a number indicates the number of amplifiers contained in a single package.

Monolithic low level

Of all the various linear functions, the audio circuit is probably the most difficult to integrate because conventional audio circuits usually require large-value capacitors, which are not easily produced in monolithic form. Even so there is quite a choice from a variety of manufacturers and a circuit might have anything from two to six stages of amplification.

One of the simplest circuits is the TAA320 shown in Fig. 1(a) in a 100V, 2W amplifier. You will see that the TAA320 itself comprises an input n-channel insulated-gate f.e.t. driving an n-p-n transistor through a separate base-emitter resistor. In the external circuit, the 180 and 3.3Ω resistors in the feedback from the loudspeaker fix the overall amplifier gain. The voltage dependent resistor suppresses potentially damaging voltage spikes across the output transistor, BD115. The circuit has a sensitivity of about 85mV input for 2W output.

Three stages of gain are found in monolithic configurations such as the TAA263, shown in Fig. 1(b). This is widely used as a basic amplifier with the addition of a load resistance between terminals two and three, and a d.c. feedback resistance between terminals three and one to set the output at the required mid-voltage. The TAA263 is designed for a 7/8V rail supply, but, in the form of the OM200, the same circuit is available for use on the 1.3 to 1.5V supply for hearing aids.

The TAA310 of Fig. 1(c) illustrates a more complex four-stage monolithic audio pre-amp. Tr_1, Tr_2 form a d.c.-coupled input feedback pair; Tr_3, Tr_4 a long-tailed pair with the signal fed into Tr_3 and the feedback into Tr_4 via the 100kΩ and 150kΩ resistors for d.c. and via the 0.027 and 25μF capacitors from the 4.7kΩ and 270Ω resistors for a.c. The four diodes at the input of Tr_5 carry out the level shifting which is necessary to set the output at half rail voltage. The TAA310 can be used in many practical circuits by the addition of suitable external components. In Fig. 1(c)

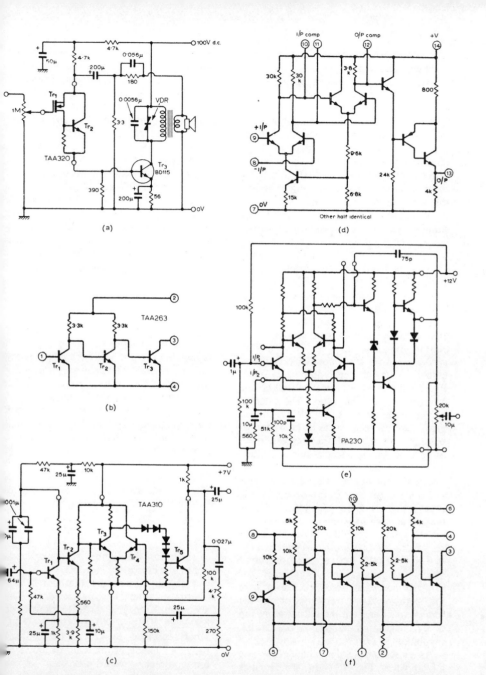

Fig. 1. Typical commercial a.f. low-level amplifier monolithic microcircuits: (a) TAA 320 two-stage m.o.s.f.e.t. input pre-amplifier in 2W crystal pickup record player; (b) TAA 263 three-stage general purpose 7V pre-amplifier; (c) TAA 310 four-stage high-gain pre-amplifier in tape playback system; (d) MC 1303P five-stage dual pre-amplifier; (e) PA 230 four-stage low-level amplifier in 'stereo' pre-amplifier; (f) TAA 370 five-stage high-gain pre-amplifier.

47

it is shown with a compensation network for a high-gain tape-replay pre-amplifier.

Five stages of amplification are to be found in the MC1303P whose internal circuit is shown in Fig. 1(d). The package contains two identical amplifiers. In previous chapters it was seen that this is very much a derivative of the 'standard' monolithic op-amp. which comprises a series of d.c.-coupled long-tail pairs with some form of d.c. level shifting to set up the output at mid-rail voltage. In use, the input signal is applied to the '+' input and suitable d.c. and a.c. feedback networks inserted between the output and the '—' input. The MC1303 has been widely used to provide front end pre-amplifiers for stereo audio systems, with different equalizing feedback networks switched in for tape replay, magnetic pickup, ceramic pickup, microphone, etc. This five-stage dual amplifier comes in a fourteen-lead dual-in-line package.

One example of a monolithic low-level amplifier that has been widely used is the PA230 shown in a typical overall circuit arrangement in Fig. 1(e). The internal circuit of the monolith (inside the shaded area) can be seen to be a conventional op-amp. with balanced input stages followed by level shifting to a single-ended push-pull output. The pair of 100kΩ resistors across one input hold the output at half rail voltage, and the d.c. feedback from the output to the other input via the 51kΩ resistor clamps the output at virtually the same voltage. The overall gain is set by the ratio of the 51kΩ resistor to the 510Ω resistor connected via a 10μF to earth across the second input. The 10kΩ resistor and 100pF capacitor in series across the feedback resistor cuts the high-frequency response, while the 75pF capacitor from the output at the top of the diagram is designed to prevent h.f. oscillation.

As a last example of monolithic low-level a.f. amplifiers, Fig. 1(f) shows the circuit of the TAA370, a six (2 × 3) stage arrangement for very high-gain hearing aid requirements. Various terminals are brought out

that give flexibility of circuit arrangements. Normally the microphone is connected to (9) with the usual feedback from (7). Terminal (8) is decoupled with a 2.2 to 10μF capacitor. The output from (7) is fed via a volume control of about 25kΩ to (1) through suitable 1μF isolating capacitors. An adjustable resistance from the positive 1.3V supply at (6) to terminal (10) enables the setting up of the output d.c. level. Terminals (5) and (2) are connected to the negative supply. The earpiece is connected from terminal (3) to (6). The whole amplifier comes in a TO-89, 10-lead flat pack. Although primarily intended for hearing aid use it is versatile and has been widely used for other types of audio circuits within the limits of its 5V supply rating.

Hybrid low level

A glance at the circuits in Fig. 1 will show you that to make practical a.f. systems with monolithic i.cs you still have to use many discrete external components, particularly capacitors. The latest progress towards doing away with external components and providing complete systems in microcircuit form has been in the field of hybrid (particularly thick film hybrid) circuits. The Japanese seem to be out ahead in this field and are providing a range of hybrids which are complete functions in themselves. They avoid the limitations of the monolithic technology by mounting subminiature capacitors, etc. inside the package.

Fig. 2 gives three examples of these thick film hybrid audio low-level amplifiers to show how the number of external components is drastically reduced.

Fig. 2(a) shows the Marconi D200? two-stage amplifier connected in an arrangement to give 62.5dB voltage gain flat from 30Hz to 20kHz with a 100kΩ input resistance. By varying the feedback network compensation can be obtained for tape replay, record play, etc.

In Fig. 2(b) there is an interesting micro circuit, the D2011, which is a single-stage tone-control amplifier. In this integration has advanced to the level where only two potentiometers and one capacitor are needed externally to give a complete treble boost/cut and bass boost/cut unit, with input and output d.c. isolation and with a high input impedance secured by boot-strapping.

Complete three-stage amplifiers are also available in thick film hybrid, as for example the D2100 equalizer shown set up for a magnetic pickup in Fig. 2(c).

In all the hybrids of Fig. 2, there are still a few external components, but the technology is such that ultimately we

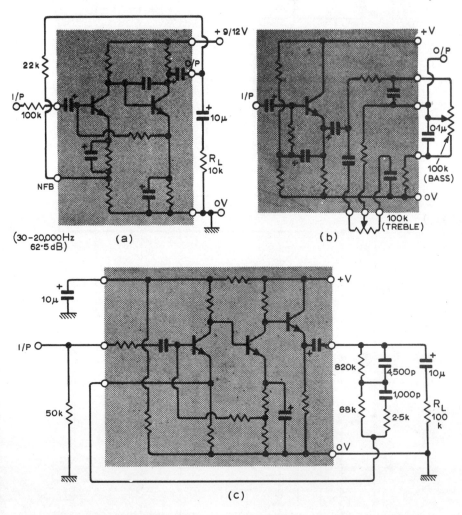

Fig. 2. Typical low-level amplifier circuit configurations now commercially available in hybrid microcircuit form and requiring minimal external components to give practical amplifier systems: (a) 'flat' pre-amplifier; (b) tone control pre-amplifier; (c) equalizer pre-amplifier for a magnetic pickup.

49

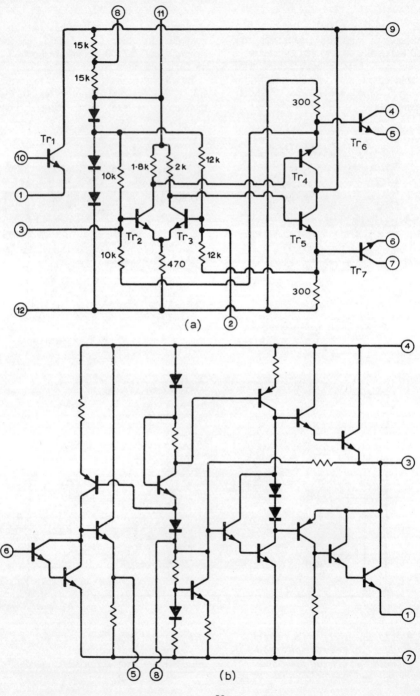

(a)

(b)

50

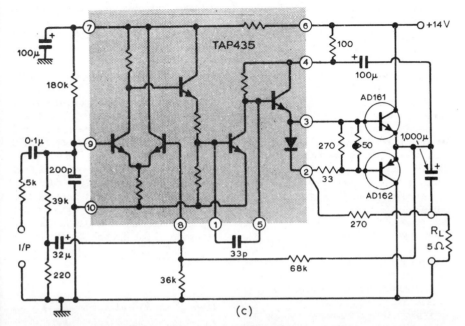

Fig.3. Typical off-the-shelf a.f. mid-level monolithic amplifier microcircuits: (a) CA3020, 9V, 500mW; (b) MFC4000P, 9V, 250mW; (c) TAA435, 14V, 250mW driver stage connected in a 15mV for 4W amplifier.

should find available completely self-contained a.f. amplifiers which have just to be wired in between input and output and connected between the positive and negative supply rails.

Medium-level monolithic

Above about 50mW power levels in an amplifier chain, the signal line impedances begin to fall rapidly (and capacitor values correspondingly begin to climb). The very small size of the silicon chip in monolithic amplifiers limits the power that can be handled without special heat sinking arrangements.

Quite a number of manufacturers have produced linear monolithic a.f. amplifiers capable of handling up to 500mW of power, and a selection of these is given in Fig. 3 to show the circuitry adopted.

Fig. 3(a) shows the well-known RCA 500mW amplifier, CA3020. The general lines of the circuit are an emitter follower, Tr_1 capable of feeding a long-tailed phase splitter driver pair, Tr_2, Tr_3, followed by emitter followers, Tr_4, Tr_5, feeding into isolated output transistors Tr_6, Tr_7. The multiple terminals and isolated input and output devices offer many circuit arrangement options.

Fig. 2(b) is the circuit of the Motorola MFC4000P, 9V, 250mW amplifier. This can be seen to be more complex than the CA3020 and does not follow conventional op-amp circuitry. It uses 14 transistors and 5 diodes, which may seem lavishly extravagant to the circuit man used to economizing on discrete semiconductors, until he remembers that many active semi-conductor devices are produced at the one

51

time on the silicon chip. Fourteen transistors in the monolith might not be more than twice as costly as producing one conventional transistor.

While the internal circuitry of these mid-level monoliths might be of interest to an advanced circuit man, the ordinary user is not really much involved. He usually only wants to know what discrete components he should connect round the monolith to get the results he wants. Fig. 3(c) gives such information for the TAA435, a 14V 250mW driver stage for a higher power amplifier. The external circuitry is shown to give 4W output from an AD161/162 complementary germanium transistor pair on a 14V supply rail, with a 15mV input to give full output.

Oddly, in this area, where you would expect hybrid microcircuits to start taking over from monoliths, there is still a dearth of commercial hybrid products. However, thick film technology is such that it seems very likely that commercial hybrids will begin to emerge as they have done in the lower level applications.

Monolithic power

Despite the difficulty of getting rid of the heat from monolithic chips, the technology has been pushed at present to the point where up to 5W audio output can be handled. Fig. 4 shows two well known examples, the MC1554 and the PA246.

From the internal circuitry of the MC1554, shown in Fig. 4(a), you can see that this is basically a long-tailed pair Tr_1, Tr_2, followed by an emitter follower, Tr_3, feeding into a buffer emitter follower, Tr_4, connected to an output transistor, Tr_5. The whole microcircuit is packaged in a ten-lead TO-5 can. In the circuit, the 39pF capacitor C_1 is a compensation capacitor to prevent instability; the network R_1, C_2 across the d.c. supply rail removes high-frequency spikes and the 10Ω resistor and the 0.1μF capacitor series network R_2, C_3 across the output is a 'Zobel' network to prevent high-frequency oscillation when a

partially inductive loudspeaker load is used.

The GE (U.S.A.) PA246 shown in Fig. 4(b) in a 5W amplifier set-up is another very well known monolithic power amplifier. The internal circuitry will be seen to be simpler than the MC1554 (certainly more easy for the less experienced circuit man to work out). Here Tr_1, Tr_2 make a long-tailed pair input stage, with Tr_2 feeding a p-n-p compound transistor Tr_3, Tr_4, Tr_5 as the lower; an n-p-n compound Tr_6, Tr_7 as the upper of an output complementary pair driving the 15Ω load through a 500μF capacitor. The d.c. setting up of the amplifier is done with the potentiometer R_4 in combination with the d.c. feedback from the output through R_1, R_2 into the base of Tr_2. The a.c. feedback is set by the ratio of R_1 to R_3.

High-power hybrid

In the power amplifier field, most of the commercial units so far have been monolithic. Thick-film hybrids do not yet feature widely in this area. However, when you get above about 5W (r.m.s.) output power, the hybrid appears up till now to be the only viable integrated circuit.

Thick-film hybrids capable of handling up to 100W of audio power have been developed. Technologies that have had to be developed for producing these include as many as nine separate screen printings, extensive use of crossover dielectric glazes, adequate thermally conductive adhesive bonds of the ceramic substrates to heat sinks, and plastic encapsulations that can withstand heavy thermal stresses. A particularly difficult problem has been the mounting of the output transistor chips to provide adequately low thermal resistance to the heat sink, and adequate thermal capacity to prevent excessive short term rise in their junction temperature.

One commercially available hybrid high-power amplifier that can be taken as typical of the breed is the Toshiba TH9013P

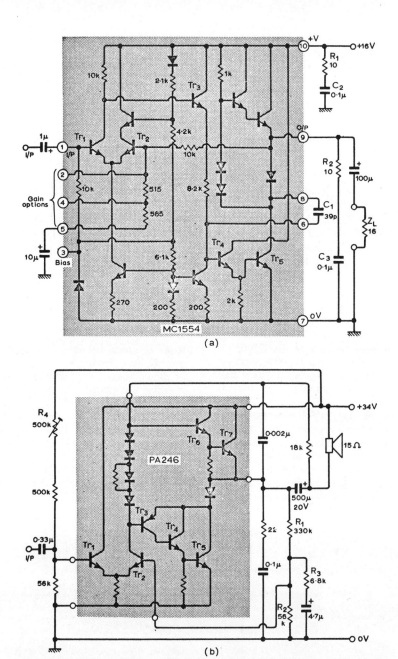

Fig. 4. Typical monolithic a.f. power amplifier microcircuits: (a) MC1554,
1.8W/16V/15Ω in a circuit with 20dB voltage gain, 10kΩ input
resistance, 100Hz to 20kHz; (b) PA246, 5W/34V/15Ω arrangement.

53

which in the circuit arrangement of Fig. 5 gives 20W output into an 8Ω speaker on a 45V d.c. rail voltage.

quired has been reduced to six including the loudspeaker and the fuse!

When using audio amplifier micro-

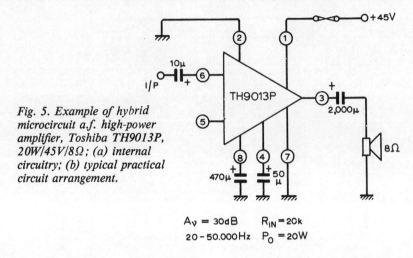

Fig. 5. Example of hybrid microcircuit a.f. high-power amplifier, Toshiba TH9013P, 20W/45V/8Ω; (a) internal circuitry; (b) typical practical circuit arrangement.

A_v = 30dB R_{IN} = 20k
20 – 50.000Hz P_O = 20W

The internal circuitry of the TH9013P would make conventional circuit men heave a sigh of relief as it follows standard discrete component practice. The hybrid consists of a long-tail input pair which feeds a driver stage which in turn drives a double complementary pair output stage. In fact the circuit could be just another of the discrete component audio amplifier variants that has appeared in the literature over the last ten years. A glance at Fig 5 shows that the number of external components re-

circuits one must not forget that many of them still have gain in the r.f. region so the user should position additional components and wiring accordingly. This point has been stressed many times in this series and cannot be overstated. Before using any of the microcircuits obtain a data sheet, most component distributors will supply you with one, and use it. If you are using a microcircuit for the first time what will you learn if you merely copy someone elses arrangement?

CHAPTER 7

Radio- and intermediate-frequency amplifiers

We tend to think of silicon monolithic technology (in which complete circuits are produced in small crystal chips little larger than the dot on a printed 'i') as being very modern. Technologically this is so, but any reader who has access to Vol. 1 of *Wireless World* could well be surprised to find in the July 1913 issue a long article by Dr. A. E. H. Tutton entitled 'Crystals as Rectifiers and Detectors' examining crystal lattice structures in detail and pointing the way to the use of 'the very best procurable single individual crystals'. Some of the semiconductors examined by Tutton such as 'perikon', 'anastase' or 'brookite' may only evoke nostalgic memories from more elderly readers. On the other hand, unexpectedly, Tutton also devoted attention to pure silicon (so important now to monolithic integrated circuits), and to such sophisticated materials as silicon carbide and liquid crystals (important now in semiconductor opto-electronics).

The celebrated H. J. Round in a reply to Dr. Tutton in the August 1913 issue was curiously prophetic in his remark 'Crystals work well as wireless receivers'. In the 1970s we have indeed reached the stage where virtually the complete receiver

circuitry can be produced in a silicon chip. The present article examines the state of the art for r.f. and i.f. amplifier microcircuits.

A survey of r.f./i.f. amplifier microcircuits in early 1971 showed about 100 commercial types available, all produced by semiconductor device manufacturers. Of these, virtually all are monolithic, although hybrid circuits are beginning to appear.

Fig. 1 gives the circuit of the Newmarket NMC809A, a thick-film hybrid r.f./i.f. amplifier. The seeing engineer's eye will note that it is a d.c. coupled feedback pair Tr_1, Tr_2, with an emitter follower buffer Tr_3, the transistors being 2N918 family devices with a typical frequency cut-off approaching 1,000 MHz. The circuit has a frequency response from d.c. to over 40 MHz. The resistor trimming possible with thick film assembly gives it a very narrow gain spread; typically ± 1dB in 22dB at 1 MHz. It can be used as a wideband amplifier or as a tuned r.f./i.f. amplifier up to 40 MHz. The separate connection to the emitter of Tr_2 allows for full decoupling for low-frequency applications, or for a peaking capacitor for top-end video expansion, and series or parallel tuned circuits for band-pass or band-reject purposes. Designed to work on 14V with

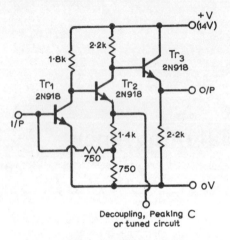

Fig. 1. Example of a thick film hybrid r.f./i.f. wideband amplifier; Newmarket Transistors NMC809A.

typically 14mA current, the NMC809A does not require any external biasing components, as bias levels are set up by resistor trimming during manufacture.

Monolithic r.f. circuits

In conventional discrete component r.f. /i.f. amplifiers it is normal to use a single transistor per stage, usually in a common-emitter arrangement, or, at very high frequencies, in a common-base arrangement. In both of these methods feedback from output to input can lead to instability and various neutralization techniques have to be used when high stage gain is called for.

Where higher stage power gain is wanted, some d.c.-coupled arrangement of two transistors can be used instead of a single transistor between tuned circuits. Three configurations often met with are the long-tail pair, the cascode arrangement and the d.c. feedback pair.

Now with discrete circuitry the single transistor common-emitter stage has such advantages in gain, noise figure and impedance matching convenience that you only come across the other arrangements mentioned where abnormal performance is required.

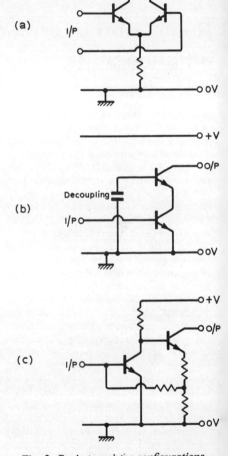

Fig. 2. Basic transistor configurations used in monolithic r.f./i.f. amplifiers; (a) long-tail pair; (b) cascode; (c) d.c. feedback pair.

56

When we come to monolithic i.cs, cost per transistor becomes less significant, being replaced by cost per stage. Here we find single transistors abandoned, and one of the three multiple-element arrays used. For ease of analysis, these are shown in basic form, without isolating and biasing networks, in Fig.2. Each has its advantages. The long-tail pair of Fig.2 (a) has fairly low noise, high power gain, high stability, simple biasing, inherently symmetrical operation, non-saturating limiting action, fast recovery from overdrive and easy interstage matching. The cascode of Fig.2(b) has low noise, high power gain, high stability, and easy interstage matching. The d.c. feedback pair of Fig.2(c) is distinctive for low noise, large signal handling capacity and low power consumption.

Long-tail pair

The long-tail pair with a resistor tail is widely used in r.f./i.f. monoliths. One example is given in Fig.3, which is the circuit diagram of the Philips TAA380A. This is an i.f. amplifier suitable for use in TV intercarrier sound circuits and f.m. broadcast receivers and comes packaged in the small multi-lead TO-5 ou/line metal can. Transistors Tr_1 and Tr_2 form a long-tail pair with tail resistor R_1 and buffer isolating emitter follower Tr_3 feeding to further long-tail pairs Tr_4, Tr_5 and Tr , Tr_8 to drive an output tuned circuit connected to terminal five. Transistors Tr_9 and Tr_{10} provide stabilized voltages for close control of d.c. bias; reference voltages being provided from selected points in the series diodes D_{1-8} which are forward biased through R_{11}.

The resistive-tail long-tail pair is used as a basic element in many other commercial monolithic r.f./i.f. amplifiers such as the General Electric PA189, RCA CA3041, 3043, Fairchild μA717, Motorola MC1350, Siemens TBA120 and the Philips TAA570. Most of these are complex multi-stage circuits to provide a

complete block of functions for a receiver.

Some monolithic multi-stage r.f./i.f. amplifiers use a transistor instead of a resistor as the constant-current source for the long-tail pair. This three-transistor type of gain block can be seen forming repetitive elements in cascode in commercial microcircuits and Fig.4, the Philips TAA350 is an example of this technique. The long-tail pair with transistor tail, Tr_1, Tr_2, Tr_3, with its output buffer emitter followers Tr_4, Tr_5 are repeated for the four stages. The bias for the tail transistor is provided from a common rail voltage defined by the forward voltage drop across the diode-connected Tr_{21} fed from the positive rail through a 2.1k Ω resistor. The differential amplification with current-driven long-tail pairs gives high a.m. rejection making the amplifier suitable for use with very simple f.m. detectors.

Several monoliths have been made which can be used in a large number of different ways. Fig. 5 gives the circuits of a number of the more common commercially available ones. These can, in most cases, be used as a cascode or a transistor-tail long-tail pair.

All the circuits of Fig.5 are basically a balanced emitter coupled transistor pair with a third transistor providing the emitter current for each of the pair. Such a configuration would be costly to fabricate with discrete components because of the difficulty of getting adequately matched balanced pairs and the need for separate biasing networks stable with temperature and supply voltage variations. With monolithic fabrication these difficulties do not arise. The different examples in Fig.5 reflect different manufacturers' design approach to versatile microcircuits with many circuit connection options.

The RCA CA3053/3028 of Fig.5(a) uses resistor networks to bias the tail transistor Tr_3. The Motorola MC1550 of Fig.5(b) features a diode in the biasing network for temperature stability; the Fairchild μA703 of Fig.5(c) uses two

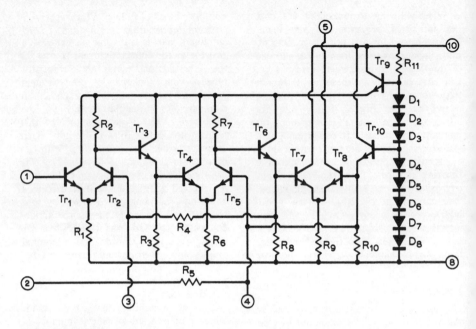

Fig. 3. Commercial i.f. amplifier microcircuit illustrative of use of resistor-tail long tail pair as basic amplifying element in monolithic microcircuit construction (Philips TAA380A).

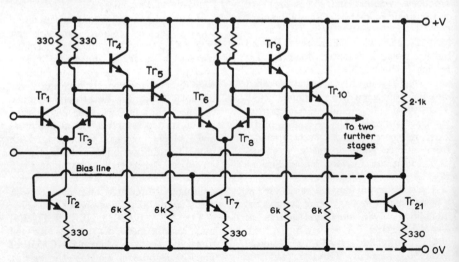

Fig. 4. Monolithic r.f./i.f. amplifier long-tail pair with transistor constant current tail (Philips TAA350).

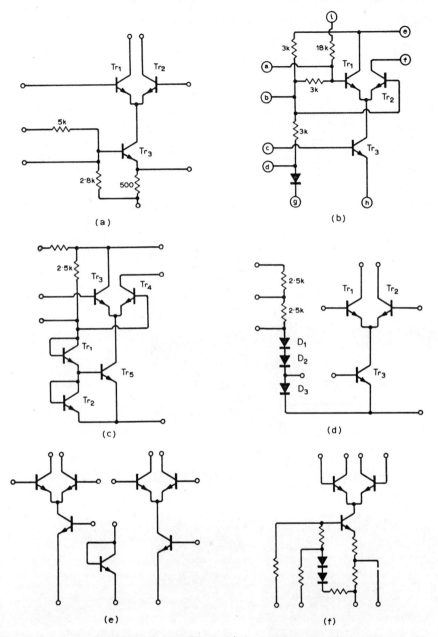

Fig. 5. Commercial single-stage monolithic r.f./i.f. amplifiers using long-tail pairs with transistor tails; (a) RCA CA3053/3028; (b) Motorola MC1550; (c) Fairchild μA703; (d) Amelco 911; (e) Signetics 511; (f) RCA 3004/3020.

biasing diodes; and the Amelco 911 (also National Semiconductors devices LM171/271/371 of Fig.5(d) uses as many as three bias semiconductors for maximum stability. Fig.5(e), the Signetics NE511, is a different approach and offers two amplifier stages in the one package together with one biasing diode. This gives the equipment designer great flexibility for special circuit requirements. Another example of extreme versatility is the RCA3004/3020 shown in Fig.5(f).

Cascode circuits

So far we have not mentioned cascode operation. It will be found that in monolithic microcircuits a true two-transistor cascode arrangement is almost never found. This is because a cascode circuit can be made up by taking a transistor-tailed long-tail pair such as Fig.5(a) and using the tail transistor Tr_3 as the common emitter input of the cascode pair and one of the balanced pair as the common-base output. Some of the circuits

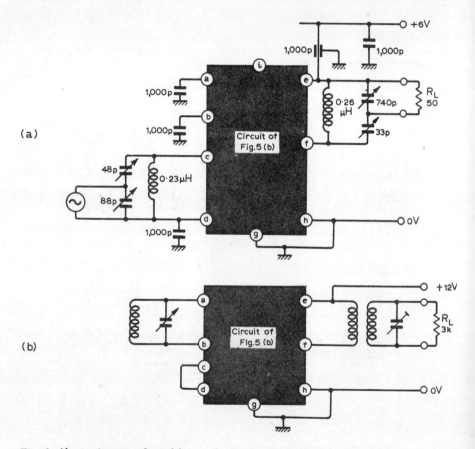

Fig. 6. Alternative cascode and long-tail pair tuned amplifier arrangements of Motorola MC1550 microcircuit; (a) cascode 60MHz, 30dB 0.5MHz bandwidth; (b) long-tail pair 10.7MHz f.m. i.f.

60

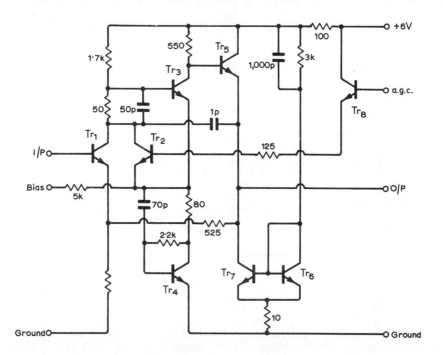

Fig. 7. Commercial r.f. amplifier monolithic microcircuit using basic d.c. coupled feedback pair configuration: Plessey SL612 r.f. (2-76MHz) tuned amplifier.

of Fig.5 have direct access to the base of the tail transistor and can be used as effectively in cascode as in long-tail pair mode (where the input is applied to one of the balanced pair). One feature not to be overlooked is that the three-transistor configuration (whether it be cascode or long-tail pair) always leaves an unused terminal which can be employed to apply automatic gain control.

Perhaps the easiest way to understand the versatility of the transistor triplet is to look at one specific example, say the Motorola MC1550 whose basic circuit is given in Fig.5(b). This microcircuit can be connected, for example, as a cascode 60MHz tuned amplifier in the arrangement of Fig.6(a) or as a long-tail pair 10.7MHz i.f. amplifier as in Fig.6(b).

D.C. feedback pair

The cascode and long-tail pair are not the only configurations used by monolithic manufacturers. The d.c. coupled feedback pair shown for discrete circuitry at Fig.2(c) above has advantages that have led to its adoption by some manufacturers. One example of this is the Plessey SL612 r.f. amplifier (Fig.7). The design is essentially an emitter coupled d.c. feedback input pair Tr_1, Tr_3 providing d.c. bias from the emitter of Tr_3 to the input of Tr_1 via a 5k Ω resistor. The d.c. coupled pair is followed by an emitter follower Tr_5 providing feedback into the emitter of Tr_1 via a 525 Ω resistor. The overall circuit gain is 20 dB Low noise is ensured by running Tr_1 at low current and good signal

61

Table 1

Directory of r.f./i.f. microcircuit manufacturers

Company	Microcircuit type numbers
Amelco (Teledyne)	911
Fairchild	μA703/717/719
General Electric (USA)	PA189
Intermetall	TAA710
Marconi-Elliott Microelectronics	M316
Mitsubishi	M5142P
Motorola	MC1100/1350/1352/1550
Mullard (Philips)	TAA350/380/380A/450/570/640
National Semiconductors	LM171/172/271/371/372/703
Newmarket Transistors	NMC 809A
Plessey	SL501/502/503/551/552/553/610/611/612
R.C.A.	CA3002/3004/3005/3006/3028/3041/3042/3043/3044/3053
S.G.S.	L103, TAA661/730
Siemens	TAA981/991, TBA120/400
Signetics	NE510/511, SE510/511

handling by the overall feedback. Effective a.g.c. control of 50dB is achieved via Tr_8 and Tr_2 and power consumption is some 15mA on a 6V supply. The circuit is optimized to give a 150MHz cut-off frequency ensuring satisfactory operation over the 2-76 MHz communications band.

To help readers see what is commercially available in the way of r.f./i.f. amplifier microcircuits, Table 1 lists the major manufacturers whose products of this type are on the U.K. market, with a selected list of types known to the author.

The wide range of microcircuits available to the equipment designer vastly simplifies the production of tuned amplifiers from 100kHz to 100MHz, whether for fixed frequency i.f. use, with high gain, low current consumption and narrow bandwidth, or for variable r.f. use, with low noise, large signal handling, a.g.c., without substantial change of characteristics, and without a performance change across the tuning band.

CHAPTER 8

Wideband amplifiers

Whatever branch of electronics you work in, you will probably one day find a need for a linear amplifier with a flat frequency response perhaps from d.c. to r.f., or even v.h.f. Such an amplifier goes variously, and sometimes loosely, under the names 'wideband', 'video', 'broadband', 'baseband' or 'linear pulse'. We will use the term wideband to cover all variants.

Wideband amplifiers are mostly used to amplify broad frequency spectrum signals (as in oscilloscope Y deflection amplifiers), but can also be used to amplify a narrow spectrum that may move about in centre frequency or be of uncertain frequency. In the days of valves you could, without too much trouble, design amplifiers up to about 10MHz bandwidth, leaning heavily on classic texts like Millman and Taub 'Pulse and Digital Techniques' (McGraw-Hill). With the arrival of transistors, the readily achievable bandwidth was pushed out to 100MHz along the lines indicated by the author in 'Elements of Transistor Pulse Circuits' (Iliffe).

By the 1970s the electronic equipment designer could choose from a wide range of complete wideband amplifiers self-contained in small metal or plastic containers about the size of a half new penny which is 17mm in diameter.

The main requirements of a wideband amplifier are good linearity (i.e. low harmonic distortion), gain stability, and uniform phase shift (i.e. low phase distortion). Wideband linear i.c. amplifiers meet these requirements well, because the transistors diffused into the silicon chip have frequency cut-offs between 300 and 1000MHz so that in the passband of the broadband amplifier, usually less than 100MHz, they are working at what is a relatively low frequency. As a result there is little differential phase shift across the transistor. Also, in a small silicon chip, no troubles can arise from parasitics in the interconnecting leads as happens in discrete component amplifiers. Finally, thermal compensating elements diffused into the chip make gain stability a minor problem. A survey of wideband amplifier microcircuits at the beginning of 1971 revealed 150 types commercially available.

Circuitry

The Ferranti ZLA10 with the circuit of Fig. 1(a) is a 12V two-transistor d.c. coupled feedback pair with a mid-band current gain of 26dB ($\times 20$). The 3dB bandwidth is d.c. to 120MHz, and output resistance is not more than 400Ω. Feedback (d.c.) is applied from terminal seven

63

to terminal six. The ZLA10 is packaged in an eight-lead TO-5 can.

The same sort of d.c. coupled feedback pair is used in the Plessey SL201 of Fig. 1(b) with the additions of an emitter resistor R_3 in the input transistor, the splitting of the output transistor emitter resistor R_7, R_8, an output resistance of 750Ω, all in an eight-lead dual-in-line package.

Another way of using three transistors in a wideband amplifier i.c. is the Sylvania SA20 of Fig.2(b). Basically it is a d.c.-coupled feedback triplet with the overall gain set by the ratio of R_6 to R_4. Typically

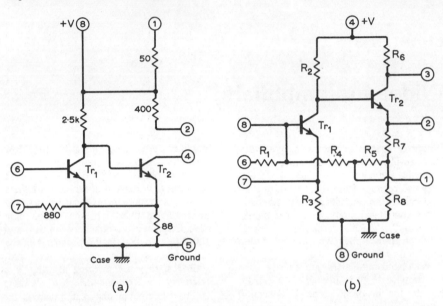

Fig. 1. Examples of two-transistor wideband amplifier microcircuits; (a) Ferranti ZLA10; (b) Plessey SL201.

and extra leadout pins one, seven and six for versatility. Designed for a 9V rail it draws 15mA supply current. With a mid-band 9dB voltage gain, it has a bandwidth of d.c. to 10MHz. It is housed in an eight-lead TO-5 package with the case connected to the negative supply terminal.

An extra transistor adds little extra cost or production difficulty in an i.c. One illustrative example is the Sprague ULN2103 of Fig. 2(a). This is a d.c.-feedback pair Tr_2, Tr_3, with an added input emitter follower Tr_1. Taking 10mA from a 12V supply, the ULN2103 has a mid-band gain of 30dB from d.c. out to a 50MHz 3dB down, an input resistance of $1.2k\Omega$,

it can be set up to provide 20dB gain to 100MHz (-3dB) while drawing 24mA from a 24V supply, and providing 12V peak-to-peak into a $1.2k\Omega$ load.

An example of the use of four transistors in a wideband microcircuit is the Signetics SE501 with the circuit of Fig.3(a). This has multi-access points that enable it to be connected as a wideband amplifier with four different gains and with bandwidths up to 50MHz without requiring the use of any external discrete components except the necessary input and output coupling capacitors.

The SE501 circuit is a d.c. coupled feedback pair Tr_1, Tr_2, with an emitter

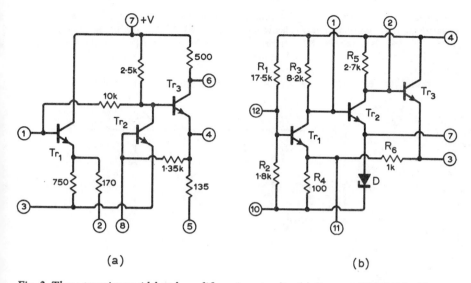

(a)

(b)

Fig. 2. Three-transistor wideband amplifier microcircuits; (a) Sprague ULN2103; (b) Sylvania SA20.

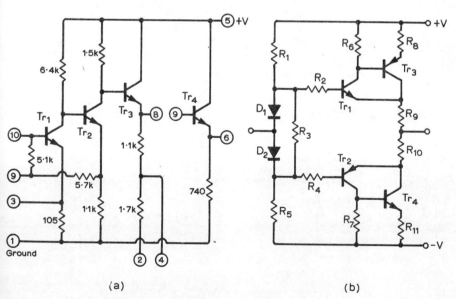

(a)

(b)

Fig. 3. Four-transistor wideband amplifier microcircuits; (a) Signetics SE501; (b) Beckman Instruments 823.

follower Tr_3 for isolation. A second isolated emitter follower stage Tr_4 is available and may be connected to increase the drive at the cost of increased power consumption. Taking 3.5mA (7.5mA with the second emitter follower used) from a 6V supply, the SE501 has an open loop gain of 46dB ($\times 200$) and bandwidth of 3MHz to 16dB ($\times 6$) and 55MHz bandwidth depending on how it is connected.

Four-transistor wideband i.cs tend to be higher gain or more versatile versions

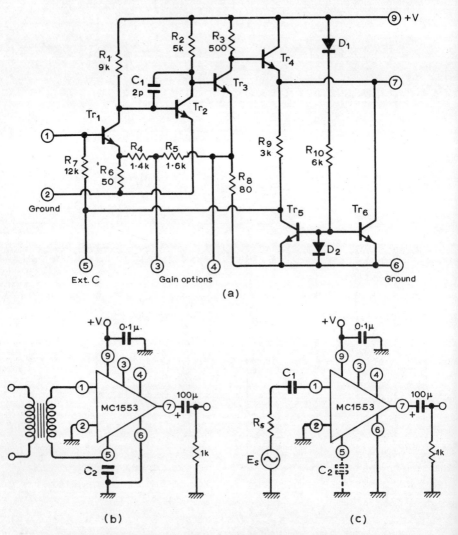

(a)

(b)

(c)

Fig. 4. A six-transistor wideband amplifier microcircuit; Motorola MC1553; (a) circuit diagram; (b) transformer input arrangement; (c) capacitor input arrangement.

of two- and three-transistor circuits. However the Beckman Instruments 823 of Fig.3(b) is an interesting departure. With ±30V power supply and an idling current of only 10mA, this thick film hybrid, unity-gain, output buffer amplifier has a 3dB bandwidth from d.c. to 4MHz, with an input resistance greater than 1kΩ and an output emitter-follower buffer Tr_4. Transistor Tr_5 is incorporated in a d.c. feedback loop to establish and stabilize the output operating point. A current-source transistor Tr_6 is used to set symmetrical positive and negative load current excursions regardless of power supply voltage, temperature or load resistance.

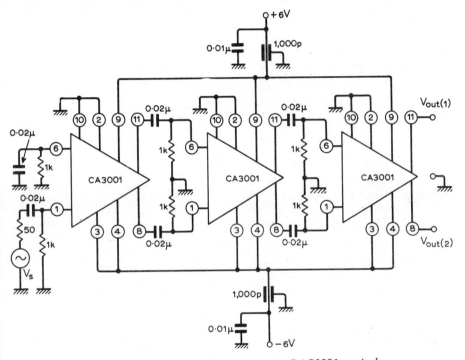

Fig. 5. Seven-transistor wideband amplifier microcircuit, RA C3001; typical arrangement in three-stage cascaded amplifier.

output resistance less than 10Ω. It can provide a 52V peak-to-peak output swing with a rise time of less than 0.1μs.

As wideband amplifier microcircuits employ more and more transistors they tend to lose the versatility of the simpler versions discussed earlier. However, even the six-transistor Motorola MC1553 of Fig.4(a) has a variety of uses.

Basically the 1553 is a d.c.-coupled feedback triplet Tr_1, Tr_2, Tr_3, with an

A second feedback loop for a.c. operation consists of resistors R_5, R_4 and R_6. This enables gains from 50 to 400 to be obtained by varying the amount of feedback, by changing external interconnection and by taking the output at various points of the circuit. Bandwidth of course falls as the gain is increased by reducing feedback.

Fig.4(b) and 4(c) show the MC1553 circuit connections for transformer and capacitor inputs, the 'dotted' capacitor C_2 in 4(c) is included when the source resistance R_s is more than 500Ω (up to 5kΩ). Typical gain options are $\times 400$ (20MHz bandwidth) leaving terminals three and four disconnected; $\times 200$ (25 MHz) connecting three to four. The low 3dB cut off frequency is set by C_1 and C_2. For practical capacitor values, it can be down around 10 to 100kHz.

The RCA CA3001, using a seven transistor circuit with a mid-band gain of 16dB and a 3dB bandwidth of 16MHz, draws only 10mA from a ± 6V (or single 12V) supply. Fig.5 shows a typical application of the CA3001 in a cascaded three stage amplifier which gives a mid-band gain of 65dB, with 3dB response limits of 10kHz and 10MHz. The need for external interstage coupling capacitors can be avoided by using output terminals twelve and seven to bring into operation internal capacitors, but this severely restricts the low-frequency end of the bandpass.

The Fairchild 702 was probably the most widely used wideband i.c. microcircuit in the second half of the 1960s. It was very similar in circuitry with its nine transistors to some of the op-amps whose circuits were given earlier in this series. With simple compensation the 702 can give a stable 40dB gain flat from d.c. to over 5MHz for 3dB down, and it can be arranged to give a usable gain up to 30MHz.

The Fairchild μA733 is an example of the extended bandwidths now attainable. It is a two-stage differential amplifier with both differential input and output available. Internal series-feedback is used to obtain wide bandwidth, low phase distortion and gain stability. Emitter follower outputs enable the device to drive capacitive loads, and all stages are current-source biased to obtain high-power supply and common mode rejection ratios.

External connections make it possible

to obtain fixed gains of 400, 100, and 10, and in addition provision is made for having the gain adjustable between 10 and 400 by selecting an external resistor. At a voltage gain of 100 the 3dB bandwidth is 90MHz.

TABLE 1
Directory of wideband amplifier microcircuits

Manufacturer	Type Number
Analogue Devices	901, 903
Beckman	
Instruments	821, 822, 823, 866
C.T.S.	
Microelectronics	CTS861
D.D.C.	VA21, VA22, VA23, VA24, CD23
Engineering	
Electronics	G106
Ferranti	ZLA10, ZLA15
Fairchild	
Semiconductors	μA702, μA712, μA719, μA733, μA751
Intronics	A501, A502
Mitsubishi	M5113, M5134
Motorola	MC1410, MC1445, MC1510, MC1545, MC1552, MC1553, MC1590, MFC4010P
Philco Ford	PA7600, PL7600, PA7605, PA7606, PA7712, PA7713, PD7712, PL7712
Plessey	SL201, SL521, SL571
R.C.A.	CA3001, CA3011, CA3012. CA3020, CA3021, CA3022 CA3023, CA3034, CA3035, CA3040
Raytheon	RC733, RM733
Sescosem	SFC2510
Siemens	TAA721, TAA722
Signetics	SE501, NE501, N5733, S5733
Silicon General	SG733, SG1401, SG1402. SG2401, SG2402, SG3401, SG3402
Sprague	ULN2103
Sylvania	SA20, SA21
Teledyne	CMC6020, CMC6021
Texas	SN2600, SN2610, SN5510, SN5511, SN7501, SN7511
Westinghouse	WC1146, WM1146

As yet there is very little standardization and, if you want to use some of the wealth of devices, you cannot avoid studying the individual products in detail. To help you at least to know where to look, a selected directory of wideband amplifier microcircuit manufacturers, whose products circulate in the United Kingdom, is appended in Table 1.

CHAPTER 9

Voltage regulators

The d.c. voltage regulator is a very common circuit in electronics as practically all equipment requires a power supply which in many cases must be stabilized. This means that a power supply's voltage must not vary with changes in mains voltage, load current or ambient temperature. Complete voltage regulator circuits are easily made in both monolithic and hybrid microcircuits.

Op-amps for voltage regulation

Although a variety of ready-made voltage regulator microcircuits are available, general purpose op-amps are now so common that many designers 'roll their own' regulators using a standard μA709, μA741, LM101 or a similar device. Fig. 1 is a typical example which will supply 12V at 100mA. The μA741 serves as a d.c. error signal amplifier. Its output current supplies the base of the series pass transistor Tr_1. The non-inverting input is held at the constant 6.2V by the zener diode. The inverting input receives an error signal proportional to the stabilized output voltage (about half) from the potential divider R_3, R_4, R_5. Fine adjustment for exactly 12V is by R_4.

Simple regulator microcircuits

Monolithic voltage regulators fall into two classes: simple medium-performance multi-option building blocks and complex high-performance complete regulators.

As a typical example of a simple regulator, Fig. 2(a) shows the circuit of the Westinghouse WM330. The compound-connected Darlington pair, Tr_1, Tr_2 has a current gain of over 10,000 and functions as the series control element. Tr_3 is the feedback amplifying transistor, while the zener diode, provides a 6.2V reference. The temperature coefficients of the V_{BE} of Tr_3 and of the zener voltage diode are equal and opposite, resulting in good temperature stability. The whole circuit is contained in a 3.5 $\times$ 3mm silicon chip mounted in an 8-pin TO-^{3} package, and is capable of handling an output current up to 1A when bolted to a heat sink. Fig. 2(b) shows the simplest way of using the WM330.

Where high output current handling is not needed, you can use one of the simple regulator microcircuits available in small-signal transistor packages. Typical of these is the G.E. (U.S.A.) D13V utility voltage regulator. See Fig. 2(c) for the circuit. This is basically a shunt regulator in which terminal three is held at a voltage above terminal one equal to the sum of V_{BE_1}, V_D, V_{BE_2}. On its own, it can be connected as a shunt regulator as in Fig. 2(d), where:

$$V_{out} = V_3 \times (R_1 + R_2)/R_2$$

The regulator adjusts the current drawn through R_3 to hold V_{out} constant. As a shunt regulator the D13V can handle up to 40mA shunt current and give a regulated output voltage up to 40V, provided the maximum permissible device dissipation of 400mW is not exceeded. For higher currents or lower standing drain from the

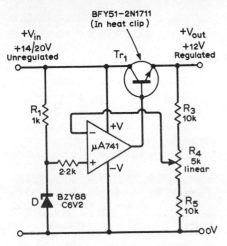

Fig. 1. Using a standard monolithic op-amp (µA741) to make up a 12V, 100mA stabilized d.c. supply.

input power supply, it can also be connected as a series regulator as in Fig. 2 (e). In this arrangement, it can control a base current of up to 40mA in the series-pass transistor Tr_3, which gives possibilities of using a power transistor for outputs up to 1A.

High-performance voltage regulators

Manufacturers have developed a wide range of more complex microcircuits using the advantages of the monolithic technology to the full and covering output voltages from 1 to 100V. Mostly these are in multi-lead TO-5, dual-in-line or flat-pack form, and usually capable of dissipating not more than about 500mW. However, higher power versions in multi-lead TO-8 and TO-3 or heat-sinked dual-in-line are becoming available.

As yet there is little standardization, although 'second sourcing' makes it possible to obtain some types from more than one manufacturer. Two regulator microcircuits have become almost industry standards in this way: the Fairchild µA 723 and the National Semiconductor LM100.

Into a silicon chip (1.3 × 1.5 × 0.18mm) the µA723 crams a power series-pass transistor, reference amplifier, error amplifier and current limiting circuitry using planar epitaxial processes.

Fig. 3 shows the internal circuitry of the 723. In this, Tr_{15}, Tr_{16} is a compound Darlington series pass element. The circuits around D_2 comprise the fixed voltage reference source. The long-tail pair Tr_{10}, Tr_{13} is a feedback amplifier with Tr_{12} as its constant current load resistor. The components Tr_1, Tr_2, R_1, R_2 and D_1 form the base biasing network for all the constant current transistors Tr_3, Tr_7 and Tr_{12}. Together Tr_3, Tr_4, Tr_5, Tr_6 provide a constant current feed for the zener D_2, with negative feedback ensuring a low output resistance for the voltage reference source. Tr_7, Tr_8, Tr_9 provide a suitable drive for the long-tail pair constant current transistor Tr_{11}.

Thus far, the 723 can be seen to be merely a refined version of the basic regulator type of Fig. 2(a). Extra features of the 723 are Tr_{14} with isolated leads offering optional uses as a feedback current limiter or as a pre-regulator. Also, both inputs to the feedback amplifier are isolated to allow additional flexibility, and the collector of the series pass transistor Tr_{16} is separated from the internal circuitry.

For full details of the performance of the µA723 the detailed data and applications sheets should be consulted, but some indication of its capabilities can be seen

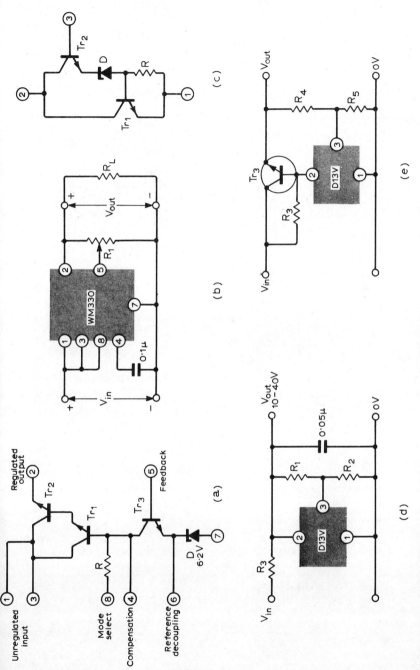

Fig. 2. *Simple voltage regulator microcircuits. (a) Westinghouse WM330; (b) connection of WM330 in practical circuit; (c) G.E. (U.S.A.) D13V utility voltage regulator; (d) the D13V as a shunt regulator; (e) the D13V as a series regulator.*

71

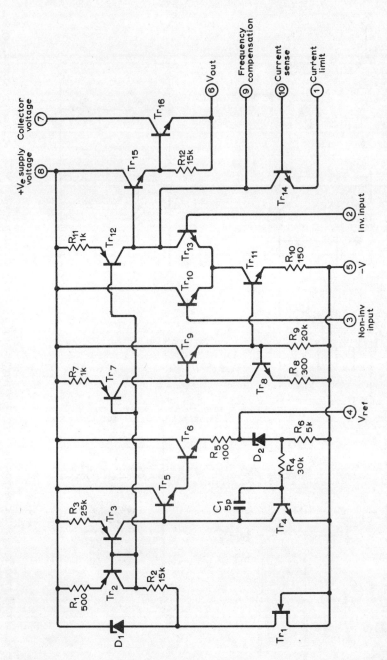

Fig. 3. Internal circuitry of industry-standard Fairchild Semiconductors μA723 voltage regulator microcircuit.

72

from the following figures. It can be used with input voltages from 9.5 to 40V and output voltages from 2.0 to 37V. It can provide output currents up to 150mA, so long as the power dissipation rating of 800mW is not exceeded. For a nominal 12V input, and 5V regulated output at a nominal load current of 5mA, V_{out} varies less than 5mV for a change of V_{in} from 12 to 15V, and less than 25mV for a V_{in} change from 12 to 40V. With V_{in} fixed at 12V for 5V output, a load current variation from 1 to 50mA will give less than 10mV variation in V_{out}. Ripple rejection is typically 80dB, i.e. 1V ripple on the input gives only 0.1mV ripple at the output. Output voltage varies with temperature less than 0.015% per C, i.e. on a 5V output less than 750 μV for 1°C change. The standby current drain of the 723 is less than 4mA, and with an external 10Ω short-circuit current limiting resistor in the output line, the output current will self limit at about 65mA.

The μA723 is supplied by many manufacturers. In the U.K. apart from Fairchild's own version, the device appears under other manufacturers' numbers such as Mullard's TBA281, S.G.S's L123 and I.T.T's MIC723.

Applications of the μA723

To illustrate the versatility of the 723, Fig. 4 gives a number of circuit arrangements using only the 723 and passive components. Monolithic i.cs such as the 723 can provide in themselves only limited voltage (up to about 40V) or current (up to about 150mA). However, external transistors can be used to extend their capabilities in this respect. For example adding an outboard 2N3055 power transistor to the basic 723 as in Fig. 5(a) raises its output current capability to over 1A,

To achieve a regulated output voltage above the limit of the 37V implicit in the 723 specification, the substrate of the microcircuit can be elevated above ground potential by tying its negative supply

terminal to a regulated voltage high enough above ground to bring the output to the required voltage. Fig. 5(b) shows how a 100V, 50mA output is obtained in this way.

Terminals three and two, the two inputs to the feedback amplifier bases, are virtually at the same potential. Thus the voltages across R_5 and R_3 are equal. Now R_3 and R_4 are equal and in series across the internal 7.15 reference voltage of the 723, so that the voltage drop across R_5 (equal to that across R_3) is 3.57V. Thus the voltage drop across R_6 is $(R_6/R_5) \times 3.57V = 102 \times 3.57/3.57 = 102V$. This sets the output line 100V above ground.

The LM100

The other workhorse voltage regulator, the LM100, uses the circuit of Fig. 6. This device contains, on a single silicon chip, the voltage reference, the feedback operational amplifier and the controlled series pass transistor to make up a voltage regulator. The voltage reference part of the circuit starts with a zener diode D_1 that is supplied by a current source (one of the collectors of the multi-collector transistor Tr_2) from the unregulated input. The output of D_1, which has a positive temperature coefficient of 2.4 mV/°C, is buffered by an emitter follower, Tr_4, which increases the temperature coefficient to +4.7mV/°C. This is further increased to +7mV/°C by the diode-connected transistor, Tr_6. A resistor divider, R_1, R_2 reduces this voltage to exactly compensate for the negative temperature coefficient of Tr_7, producing a fully temperature-compensated output of 1.8V at the base of Tr_8.

The transistor pair Tr_8, Tr_9 form the input stage of the operational amplifier. The gain of this stage is made high by the use of a current source (one of the collectors of Tr_2) as a collector load for Tr_9. The output of this stage drives a compound emitter follower Tr_{11}, Tr_{12}, to supply a regulated output voltage at terminal one. An additional transistor, Tr_{10} is used to permit limitation of the output current of

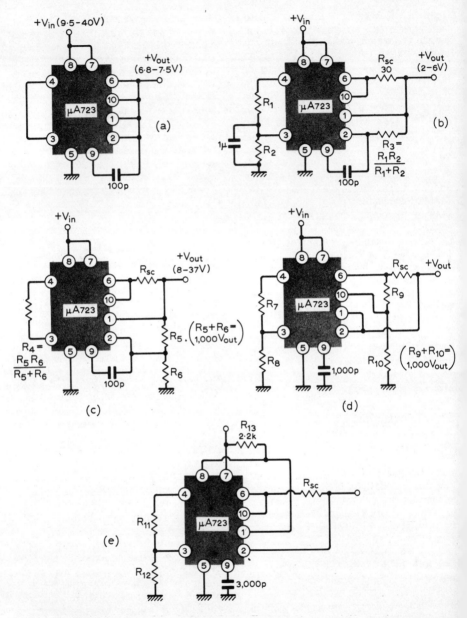

Fig. 4. Versatility of commercial voltage regulator microcircuits illustrated in typical circuit connection options for standard µA723. (a) Nominal 7.15V output with only one external capacitor; (b) low voltage (+2 to +6V) output; (c) high voltage (+8 to +37V) output; (d) foldback current limiting arrangement; (e) pre-regulated low voltage output.

74

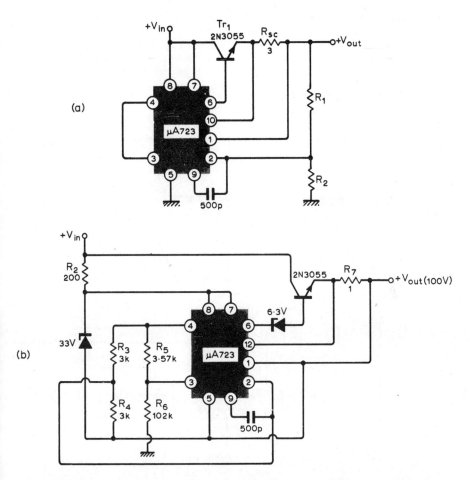

Fig. 5. Typical uses of external transistors to extend output capabilities of standard voltage regulator microcircuit (μA723). (a) high-current series-pass external transistor; (b) 'floating' high voltage (100V, 50A) output.

Tr_{12}. This current limit is determined by an external resistor connected between terminals one and eight, with a value between 10 Ω for 30mA current limit to 30 Ω for 10mA. As for the rest of the circuit, Tr_1, Tr_3, Tr_5 are part of a bias stabilization circuit for Tr_2 to set its collector currents at the desired values. Resistors R_9, R_4 and zener diode D_2 serve the sole function of starting the regulator.

Finally D_3 is a clamp diode which keeps Tr_9 from saturating on feedback overload.

The LM100 can be obtained in an 8-lead TO-5, dual-in-line or flat-pack form. The terminal numbers in Fig. 6 refer to the TO-5 version. The basic LM100 is specified for a -55 to $+125°C$ temperature range. The same device also appears as the LM200 for -25 to $+85°C$, and LM300 for 0 to $+70°C$. The LM100 is available from a

75

number of manufacturers, usually under a related number as LA100 (Nucleonic Products), or SG100 (Silicon General). Also, we find alternative types, such as the RCA CA3055, with different internal circuitry but which are completely interchangeable with LM100 having the same pin connections and performance.

very closely the pattern of the 723 as shown in Figs. 4 and 5, and will not be detailed here. However, an illustration of how the LM100 can be used in conjunction with general purpose op-amps to produce a practical regulated double-rail bench supply for working with op-amps is given in Fig. 7.

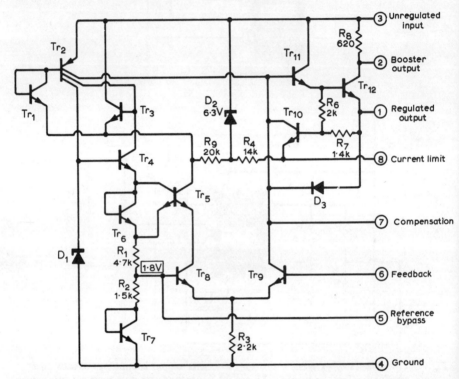

Fig. 6. Internal circuitry of industry-standard National Semiconductors LM100 voltage regulator microcircuit.

Performance-wise the LM100 is not dissimilar to the μA723. Its input voltage range is 8.5 to 40, and output 2.0 to 30V. Its load regulation is better than 0.5% for a current output from 1 to 10mA. Its line regulation is less than 0.2%/V, and its standby current on no load less than 3mA.

Applications of the LM100

Circuit applications of the LM100 follow

Fig. 7(a) is the mains step-down, rectifying and smoothing unit to give positive and negative 24V unregulated d.c. rails, A and B, with a ground rail G.

Fig. 7(b) shows the section to produce stabilized positive and negative 20V rails, C and D. The LM100 is connected to give the positive rail C directly. An op-amp, A_1, with its non-inverting input connected to the ground rail through a 10kΩ resistor

76

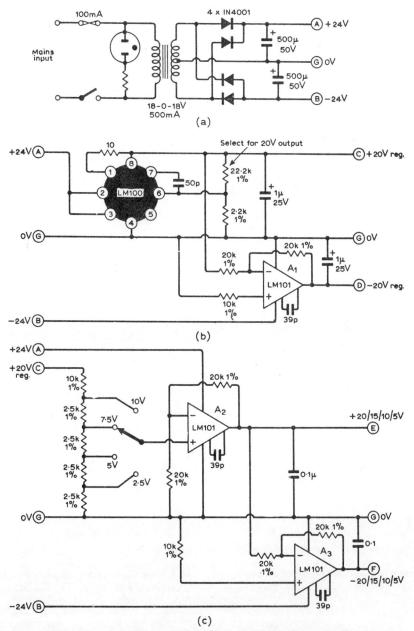

Fig. 7. Application of LM100 in regulated double ($\pm$) rail bench power supply for use with linear microcircuits: (a) rectifying-smoothing giving $\pm$24V unregulated; (b) fixed $\pm$20V regulated section; (c) switchable $\pm$5, 10, 15, 20V section.

77

has its input virtual earth at ground potential. The 20kΩ input resistor from the +20V rail to the inverting input and the 20kΩ resistor from the inverting input to the output establish the output at −20V, to provide the negative regulated rail, D.

The third section of the system shown in Fig. 7(c) is designed to provide a further two stabilized positive and negative rails, switchable through the range ±20, 15, 10 and 5V. The regulated +20V applied at the input to the ladder network of resistors, sets up selectable reference voltages of 2.5, 5.0, 7.5 and 10.0V which can be applied to the non-inverting input of the op-amp, A_2. The 20kΩ resistors from the inverting input to ground and to the output set up the output voltage of A_2 at $(20+20)/20=2$ times the input voltage on the non-inverting input. This gives a positive output rail E whose voltage can be set at 5, 10, 15 or 20V. The op-amp A_3 is used to produce an inverted output equal and opposite in sign to E. Thus F gives an output of −2.5, 5, 10, 20V corresponding to the voltages on E.

Although the op-amps shown in the design are LM101, they could equally well be any standard device such as the µA709 or µA741.

Special-purpose voltage regulators

So far we have discussed only general-purpose voltage regulators which can be adapted to many different voltage requirements. There is growing up, however, a range of devices specially fabricated for a single use.

An example of these is the Philips TAA550, an integrated monolithic two-terminal voltage stabilizer in a two-lead TO-18 can which is specially designed to provide the supply voltage for variable capacitance diodes in television tuners independent of supply voltage and temperature variations. With a nominal stabilized voltage of 33V, all these require are a series resistance to the unregulated power supply

and a shunt capacitor. They take typically 5mA of current.

Another useful example of special-purpose regulators is the LM309, which is a complete 5V regulator on a single silicon chip. Designed for local regulation on digital logic cards, the 309 neatly eliminates distribution problems caused by single central-point regulation in the system. No external components or adjustments are required. In a TO-5 package, it handles currents up to 200mA, and in a TO-3 over 1A.

Hybrid voltage regulators

We nowadays have a rather impressive range of monolithic voltage regulators readily commercially available, and yet hybrid microcircuit manufacturers continue to introduce new regulators. Why is this? Well, you can build higher power hybrid regulators than you can mono-lithic. But the main advantage of hybrid assembly is that hybrid techniques permit you to 'trim on test' during manufacture, and adjust the output voltage much more exactly than can be achieved in mono-lithics. Also any high-frequency compensating capacitors can be included in the package to give you a truly self-contained circuit requiring no additional external components.

Fig. 8 is the circuit of the General Instruments NC562 hybrid regulator. Typical of hybrid voltage regulators, this circuit is thermally and electrically more efficient than an equivalent monolithic version because of the use of parallel pass transistors Tr_6, Tr_7 with low saturation resistance. The control amplifier uses high-gain n-p-n and p-n-p transistors, Tr_1-Tr_2 and Tr_3-Tr_4, to ensure high open-loop gain and minimum standby current. A junction f.e.t., Tr_5, forms a constant current source to drive Tr_6 and Tr_7 bases under feedback control by transistor Tr_1. The zener reference element D_2 is compensated by D_1 to

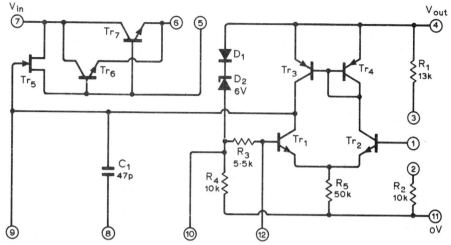

Fig. 8. Circuit of hybrid voltage regulator, General Instruments NC562.

provide excellent temperature characteristics for the regulator, and the unit is encapsulated in a high-dissipation 12-lead TO-8 package.

If terminals one, two and three are connected together, and terminal eight is connected to twelve, and six to four, and if a supply of more than 13V is connected to terminal seven then the output from terminal four is a precise stabilized 12V at up to 800mA with 0.1Ω output resistance.

By connecting a variable potentiometer across one-two-three, the output can be adjusted between 10 and 20V. A current limiting circuit can be connected at terminals four, five and six and a decoupling capacitor for the reference element at terminal ten.

State of the art

Except for the general adoption of the $\mu A723$ and the LM100, there is no effective standardization of voltage regulator microcircuits. Hitherto most of the regulator microcircuits available have been single-rail only, but a fairly recent development has been the appearance of double-rail types such as the Motorola Semiconductor's $\pm 15V$ MC1567.

Finally, a likely development is that hybrid manufacturers will take basic chips like the LM100 and incorporate them with all the necessary extra components to produce self-contained three-terminal packages, that only have to be inserted between the unregulated supply and the regulated output lines with a common earth line.

CHAPTER 10

Amplitude modulated radio receivers

Despite the increasing number of f.m. sets in use, most domestic and car radio receivers are still a.m. only, usually covering the m.w. band, 540 to 1640 kHz, and sometimes also the l.w. band, 155 to 280 kHz. We will take a look at the application of linear microcircuits in this field.

When off-the-shelf linears first began to come into the hands of set designers in the mid 1960s, they offered a possible alternative to the use of six to ten separate transistors in a conventional superhet circuit, which had by then become almost a way of living. This market presented a tempting large-scale outlet to semiconductor manufacturers, and as a result a lot of effort has gone into trying to develop microcircuits for a.m. receivers.

The ideal microcircuit design for this purpose would be a device with all active and passive circuit components incorporated with the exception of the aerial, tuning control and indicator, volume control, loudspeaker and power supply. This may come some day, but for the present we must be satisfied with microcircuits which do not go as far as this.

Most approaches to the problem started from the conventional superhet circuit arrangement and were aimed at producing monolithic silicon chips containing as many of the transistors, resistors and capacitors of the discrete designs as possible. However, one school of design (using phase-locked-loop techniques to be described later) has abandoned the conventional superhet.

Partitioning superhets

If you cannot reach the ideal solution of the single chip, then you are faced with the problem of how to break the superhet down into sections. Receiver designs using i.cs have followed three main paths:

Discrete approach, in which only the active components are integrated. This fails to make use of the full potential of the monolithic circuit art because separate passive component counts are not reduced.

Functional approach, in which single functions of the receiver are fabricated in separate monolithic circuits and are assembled with additional discrete components to form a complete radio.

System approach, in which multiple receiver functions (e.g. the mixer, oscillator and i.f. amplifier) are fabricated on the monolithic circuit chip.

The discrete approach soon proved to have no advantages over discrete assembly, and is of historical interest only. The functional approach, too, proved uncompetitive with discrete assembly but, although it has now been abandoned. we will take a look at one example of it as a significant step towards current practice.

Single i.f. stage

Fig. 1 (a) shows the internal circuitry of the Motorola MC1550G, a versatile common-emitter, common-base cascode-circuit high-frequency amplifier capable of 30dB gain at 60MHz but which can be used for a 470kHz i.f. amplifier in the circuit of Fig. 1 (b). •

It will be seen that all the resistors and semiconductors for the single stage have been integrated, and apart from the LC bandpass circuits, only three external capacitors are required.

One chip, r.f. in to a.f. out

The Mullard TAD100, whose circuit diagram is shown in Fig. 2, was one of the first i.cs designed specifically for a.m. radios. The design aim was a low-cost integrated circuit (not too expensive for economic service replacement), with performance not worse than that of conventional discrete-component receivers, and in standard 14-lead dual-in-line package. It incorporates no fewer than 11 transistors and three diodes, together with many of the passive components from the mixer to the audio pre-amplifier.

Tr_1 and Tr_2 form a long-tail pair mixer stage, and Tr_3 is the local oscillator. Tr_4, $_5$ and Tr_6 comprise a high-gain wideband amplifier for i.f. amplification, and Tr_7 is a transistor detector. Tr_8 and $_9$ are a long-tail pair audio pre-amplifiers and Tr_{10}, Tr_{11} a Darlington common collector audio driver stage. Diodes D_1, D_2 in parallel, back to back, across the oscillator transistor collector coil terminals, serve to stabilize the local oscillator. D_3 is a level shifting d.c. coupling diode to the input of the driver stage.

Typically the TAD100 takes about 20mA quiescent current in a 9V circuit. Its sensitivity for a 26dB signal-to-noise ratio (a standard index) is typically 25 μV at input terminal (1). Its a.g.c. range controlled by feedback from (8) to (1) is typically 62dB change in r.f. input voltage for only 10dB expansion in audio output. For 10mV audio at the detector load, less than 6 μV r.f. input is required at the input.

You can see how the TAD100 is used in practice in the 9V broadcast-band receiver arrangement of Fig. 3. A 180/280pF gang capacitor tunes the rod aerial coil L_1 and the oscillator coil L_3. The r.f. input is connected across (1) and (13), and the local oscillator drive feeds into (13); a.g.c. is fed back from (8) into (1) via a decoupling network and L_2. From (3) a 560 Ω resistor to the negative supply (shunted by a series 56 Ω resistor in series with 0.047 μF) forms the tail of the input long-tail pair. The mixer output from (14) feeds into the input (a) of the 470kHz LP1175 block filter, which is a combination of two tuned LC circuits with a ceramic resonator as shown separately inset in Fig. 3. The LP1175 gives the typical normal 6dB bandwidth of 7 to 8kHz and a significant improvement in skirt selectivity over conventional fixed-tuned i.f. transformers.

From the filter output (b), the i.f. signal passes into (10) and is amplified and detected to reappear from (8) to provide the audio drive to the top end of the volume control and the a.g.c. signal to be fed back to (1). From the volume control slider the audio is fed into (4) and reappears amplified at (6) to drive the output stage. In this design the output transistors are a discrete n-p-n/p-n-p pair in single-ended push-pull, capacitor-coupled to a 4Ω loudspeaker to give over 1W output.

At first sight there seems still to be a very large number of components outside the microcircuit, but it should be noted that most of them are passive and of wide tolerance, and unlikely to give trouble in assembly. Also the use of a block i.f. filter requiring no 'adjustment' simplifies set assembly.

One chip, r.f. in to i.f. out

The TAD100 was designed to integrate as

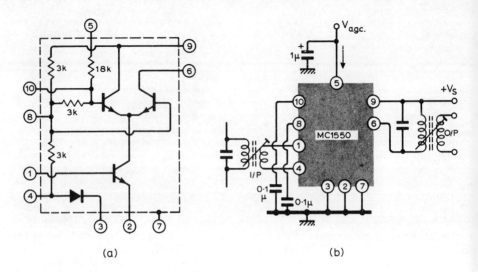

Fig. 1. Example of single-stage integration; (a) internal circuit of Motorola MC1550G r.f./i.f. amplifier; (b) MC1550G in single i.f. stage.

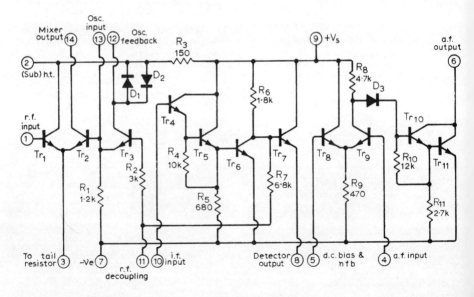

Fig. 2. Internal circuitry of Mullard TAD100 a.m. radio receiver microcircuit handling signal from local oscillator via mixer up to audio driver stage.

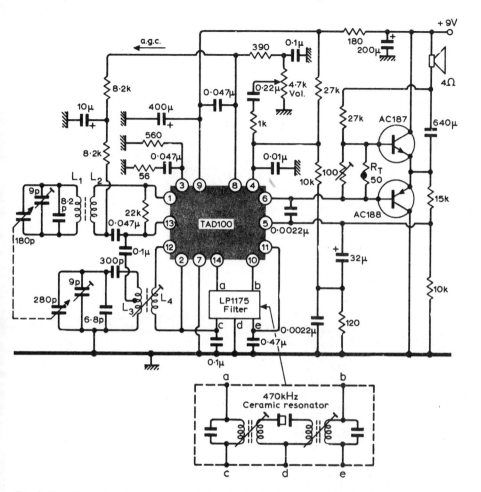

Fig. 3. Broadcast-band a.m. receiver design (9V) utilizing TAD100 microcircuit.

much of the a.m. receiver as practicable. The a.f. output stage was left out because of dissipation limitations in the package used. A different partitioning was adopted by S. G. S. in their TBA651 linear integrated circuit that processes the whole high-frequency signal in a.m. receivers. It consists of five stages: r.f. amplifier, mixer, oscillator, i.f. amplifier, and a.g.c. control and voltage regulator and was designed primarily for high quality domestic and car radios. This explains the inclusion of

a separate r.f. amplifier stage, and also the ability to work from voltage rails of 4.5 to 18V. The circuit is packaged on a 'split' (staggered pins) 16-lead dual-in-line.

In Fig. 4 you will find details of the internal circuitry of the TBA651. Tr_1 is an r.f. amplifier; Tr_6 and Tr_7 the mixer; Tr_5 (with Tr_4) the local oscillator; Tr_2 and Tr_3 the a.g.c. control on the r.f. amplifier; Tr_8 and Tr_9 (with Tr_{10} tail current source), Tr_{11}, Tr_{12}, Tr_{13} the i.f. amplifier; and Tr_{14}, Tr_{15}, Tr_{16}, Tr_{17} a voltage regulator circuit providing three output voltages to set the d.c. bias conditions of the various transistors.

An a.m. car radio circuit using the TBA651 is given in Fig. 5. A three-ganged permeability unit tunes the aerial input, r.f. amplifier and local oscillator circuits. A double-tuned i.f. bandpass circuit L_4 and L_5 connected between (5) and (13) in series with the input to the i.f. amplifier section provides part of the required i.f. selectivity and the balance is provided by the single-tuned circuit L_6 at the i.f. output (10). The input LC filter can be replaced by a ceramic-plus-LC filter similar to the LP1175 for greater skirt selectivity.

In Fig. 5 it will be seen that a conventional a.m. diode detector is used externally to the TBA651; unlike the TAD100 where a transistor detector is included in the microcircuit. After the volume control, a number of arrangements are possible. In Fig. 5 the monolithic TAA611/B is used to drive a pair of output transistors (medium power, with a current gain at 3A of greater than 20) to give 5W output. A number of completely integrated 5W, 12V audio amplifiers are coming on the market with sufficient gain to be driven direct from the volume control in applications such as these, and ultimately we should see two-chip complete radio receivers.

Phase-locked-loop alternative to the superhet

The difficulty of microminiaturizing frequency selective circuits has shown the lack of adaptability of the conventional superheterodyne system to an integrated radio receiver, particularly in the lower frequency bands. Because of this, designers are exploring systems that do not call for such fixed-tuned frequency selective circuits.

One area where there is much activity is the p.l.l. (phase locked loop) receiver. This has been around as an idea since the early 1930s, when H. de Bellescize published an article on 'La Reception Synchrone' in *e'Onde Electrique,* Vol. 11, pp. 230-240, June, 1932. Nothing came of this, but in *Electronic Engineering,* pp. 75-76, March, 1947, D. G. Tucker raised the matter again in 'The Synchrodyne'. The p.l.l. receiver also goes variously under the names of 'Homodyne', 'Synchronous Detector', 'PL' (phase locked) and 'PC' (phase coherent).

Fig. 6 (a) shows the principle of the phase locked loop. A carrier of amplitude A_c frequency f_c, and phase ϕ_c, with modulation S is applied to a phase detector which compares this input with the unmodulated output from a local oscillator of amplitude A_0, frequency f_0, phase ϕ_0. If the local oscillator frequency is adjusted to equal the carrier frequency, the phase detector gives an output proportional to the phase difference $\theta = \phi_c - \phi_0$ between the input and oscillator phases. This output is then passed through a low-pass filter and an amplifier and fed back to vary the control voltage on the local oscillator in such a way as to reduce the phase difference between the two signals. The end result is that the local oscillator phase advances or retards until it is in phase with the carrier phase. The local oscillator need not be tuned exactly to the carrier frequency for the phase locked loop to operate. There is a capture effect, in that the local oscillator need be brought only roughly to the carrier frequency and the system then pulls into frequency and phase synchronism with the carrier.

The most elementary p.l.l. receiver can consist of a voltage-controlled local oscillator, a mixer (phase detector) and an audio amplifier with the audio signal fed back to control the local oscillator. In the mixer the signal carrier is converted to a zero-frequency intermediate frequency, the output from the mixer containing only demodulated information from the sidebands.

There are now indications from theoretical and experimental investigations that

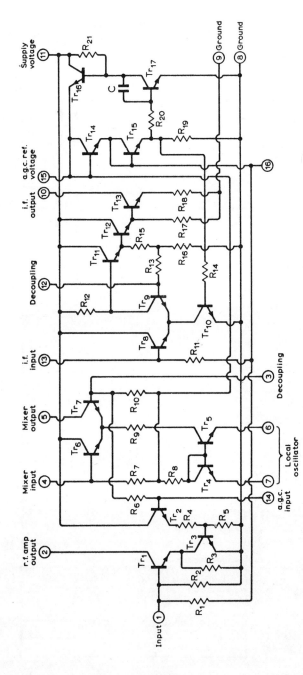

Fig. 4. internal circuitry of S.G.S. TBA651 a.m. radio receiver microcircuit handling
signal from r.f. amplifier up to i.f. output.

85

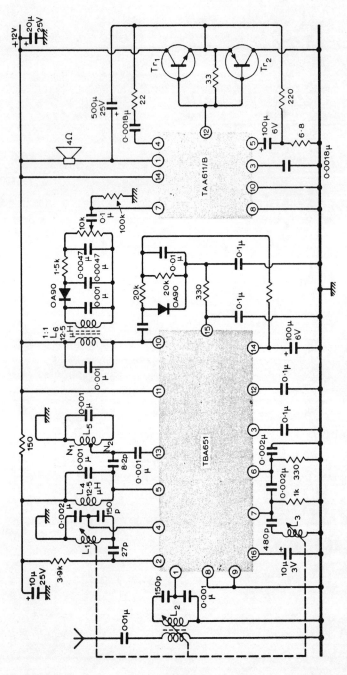

Fig. 5. 12v broadcast-band a.m. car radio receiver utilizing TBA651 microcircuit.

86

p.l.l. receivers are performance and cost-wise competitive with (even perhaps better than) conventional superhets. And the important thing is that the fixed-tuned LC bandpass circuits of the superhet are avoided.

The p.l.l. receiver has some distinctive advantages over the superhet, apart from the lack of i.f. coils. Any interference will not be synchronous with the local oscillator, so that the mixer output resulting from an interference signal will be a beat note suppressed by the audio filtering. Also there is no image response in the system

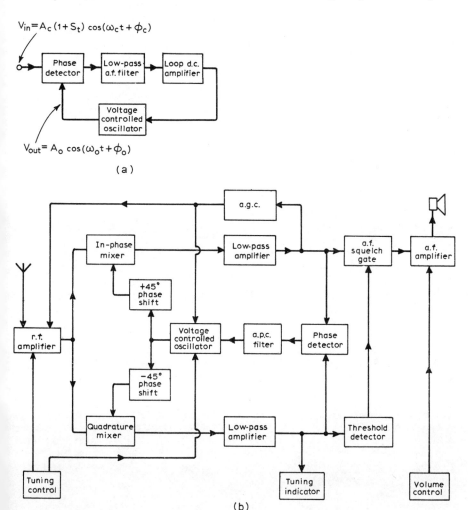

Fig. 6. The phase-locked-loop receiver alternative to the superhet; (a) basic phase-locked-loop; (b) system layout for phase-locked-loop a.m. receiver capable of implementation in microcircuit form.

because the intermediate frequency is zero. These nearly ideal selectivity characteristics and the lower possible thresholds of reception have led to the wide use of p.l.l. receivers in difficult signal environments such as reception from artificial satellites where low signal level, doppler shift and oscillator drift present problems. In the more mundane field of a.m. receivers, p.l.l. techniques have hitherto been prohibitively expensive, but now monolithics are appearing which would seem to make the p.l.l. domestic receiver a strong contender.

The National Semiconductor LM565 phase-locked-loop (although essentially a high quality professional microcircuit) is indicative of the sort of circuit that will soon become available to set designers. It contains a stable, highly linear voltage controlled oscillator and a double balanced phase detector. The v.c.o. (voltage controlled. oscillator) frequency is set with an external resistor and capacitor, and a tuning range of 10:1 can be obtained with the one capacitor.

Fig. 6 (b) shows the outline of an a.m. p.l.l. receiver system that could be put together with currently available monolithic microcircuits. The r.f. input from the aerial is passed through a tunable r.f. amplifier. Unfortunately this still involves some form of inductance. The main purpose of the r.f. amplifier is to reject harmonics of the signal frequency to which the mixer might respond. The bulk of the receiver gain will still be at audio frequencies.

From the r.f. amplifier the input signal passes to the in-phase mixer (which can be a simple diode bridge) where it is mixed with the output from the v.c.o.—not directly but with a +45° phase-shift. The frequency of the v.c.o. will have been adjusted to approximately the right value from the tuning control. The in-phase mixer acts as a phase (and frequency) detector. The output then passes through the low pass amplifier and back via the second phase detector, the a.p.c. (automatic phase control) filter to lock the v.c.o. to the frequency and phase of the r.f. input.

The output from the r.f. amplifier is also fed into the quadrature mixer where it is mixed with a −45° phase shifted output from the v.c.o. Through the second loop amplifier and the path phase detector-a.p.c. filter it also helps to lock the v.c.o. on signal. The quadrature signal channel can be used to drive a visual tuning indicator.

A difficulty with p.l.l. receivers is that an annoying beat note 'heterodyne whistle' is heard as the receiver is tuned between stations. This can be eliminated by a threshold detector and a.f. squelch gate. When the receiver is off-tune, there is a significant output from the quadrature channel which activates the threshold detector and holds the squelch gate closed thus suppressing audio output. On tune, the quadrature channel output falls to virtually zero, the squelch gate is opened and audio output passes to the a.f. amp and the louspeaker.

Finally, an a.g.c. signal is taken from the in-phase channel via the a.g.c. amplifier to control the gain levels of both the r.f. amplifier and the local oscillator.

There is a very full discussion of the p.l.l. receiver described above in L.P. Chu 'A phase-locked a.m. radio receiver' in *Trans. I.E.E.E.* Vol. BTR 15, No. 3, pp 300-308, Oct, 1969. For the whole subject of phase-locked-loops an excellent standard reference is 'Phaselock Techniques' by F.M. Gardner, John Wiley and Sons, 1966.

CHAPTER 11

F.M. radio receivers

The electronics design engineer working in the domestic radio field is turning away from discrete transistors to the numerous special-purpose linear i.cs which are now available. However, it is evident that an i.c. for domestic radio application must meet quite a number of special constraints.

It must be lower cost to the set manufacturer than discrete-component assemblies.

Must be capable of being 'second sourced'.

Its throw-away value must not be too high to permit economic servicing.

Reliability should be higher than discrete assemblies.

It should be able to work over widely different voltage rails (which usually means internal voltage regulator stages).

Current consumption should be as low as discrete designs because dry-battery operation is often required. (This can conflict with the different voltage rail requirement.)

It should be designed for easy handling, testing, installation and removal.

Before the linear i.c. arrived, a.m./f.m. set manufacturers had already had experience of block modules made with discrete components in the Mullard 'LP' range (LP1169/79 f.m. tuner blocks and LP1164/65, 1170/71 a.m./f.m. i.f. blocks).

As a result, they had already solved some of the assembly problems involved in changing over from traditional separate component assemblies to the use of functional assemblies—which is after all what i.cs are.

Partitioning a.m./f.m. receivers

Different manufacturers adopt different approaches to the problem of how to divide up receiver functions for the separate i.c. packages required to make up the set. Until some degree of standardization is reached all we can do at this stage is to look at some typical examples.

If you are interested in the detailed problems of partitioning f.m. domestic radios, you will find a useful discussion of the topic in 'A.M./F.M. monolithic receivers' by P. E. Hermann, L. H. Hoke, R. L. Petrosky and R. Wood (of Philco-Ford) in *I.E.E.E. Transactions on Broadcast and Television Receivers,* July 1968, Vol. BTR-14, No. 2 pp. 95-103.

Initially set designers tried to use general purpose professional linear i.cs (such as the μA703 and MC1550) for domestic receivers, but were unsuccessful because they were too costly.

Next, industry turned to developing special i.cs for high-performance professional f.m. applications, such as the RCA CA3076 10.7MHz high-gain amplifier limiter and the CA3075 amplifier limiter detector. These could be integrated into excellent high-gain f.m. systems but the assembly costs could not compete with conventional discrete transistor assembly in domestic f.m. sets. (A full description of the CA3075/6 and their applications can be found in 'High-performance integrated circuits for high-gain f.m.-i.f. systems' by R. T. Peterson in *I.E.E.E. Transactions on Broadcast and Television Receivers*, Nov., 1970, Vol. BTR-16, No. 4 pp 257-263.)

Another interesting development that pointed the way to current practice was the Fairchild set of i.cs μA717, 718, 719, and 720. These were all the same basic

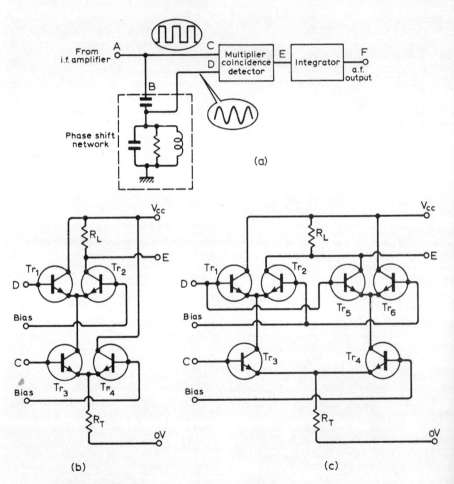

(a)

(b)

(c)

Fig. 1. Coincidence (quadrature) f.m. detector system suited to i.cs in f.m. receivers; (a) simplified block diagram; (b) practical i.c. realization of half-wave detector; (c) full-wave detector.

monolithic chip with different internal metallizing interconnection patterns which produced devices for various television, f.m. and a.m./f.m. applications. More details of these are given in 'Novel multi-purpose I.i.cs introduce new concepts into circuit design' by David Bingham in *I.E.E.E. Transactions on Broadcast and Television Receiver*, July, 1967, Vol. BTR-13, No. 2 pp 108-115.

Detection

Over the years many different types of f.m. detection have been used. Most of them, such as the 'Fremodyne' (single detuned LC circuit drive to detector), the 'Travis' (two LC circuits detuned on each side of i.f.), and the 'super-regenerative' detector, have fallen out of favour. With discrete transistors, the two systems with the widest commercial use are the Foster-Seeley discriminator (common in the U.S.A.) and the ratio detector (common in Europe). Neither of these is ideally suited to monolithic i.cs because they require carefully tuned balanced LC circuits. With i.cs they are tending to be replaced by the coincidence (quadrature) detector requiring only one tuned LC circuit; by the phase-locked-loop detector, dispensing with inductances altogether; and by the diode-pump detector (also inductorless).

The diode pump or pulse-counter detector is attractive because it is so easy to set up, but to be really efficient it calls for a low intermediate frequency, around 100kHz, which tends to rule it out for low-cost domestic receivers.

The coincidence detector appears to be preferred by most designers for 10.7MHz /i.f.,f.m. detection with i.cs. Fig.1 illustrates its working. In Fig.1(a), the 10.7MHz signal, built up to a square wave in a preceding limiting amplifier, is fed into terminal A. From A it passes direct to one terminal C of the coincidence multiplier in one direction and it is also split off into a second channel B which contains a single tuned circuit (externally connected to the

i.c.), the action of which restores the 10.7MHz square wave to sine-wave form at terminal D. Thus both the square wave and the sine wave are fed to the multiplier circuit. The signal frequency modulation varies the instantaneous frequency of both signals and, since the sine wave is subjected to a phase displacement due to the action of the tuned circuit, the coincidence detector produces an output at E consisting of a series of pulses of mean value proportional to the modulation frequency. Thereafter the integrator (a capacitor shunting the output resistance of the coincidence detector) recovers the audio from the f.m. r.f. signal and provides the necessary de-emphasis or top cut (European time constant 50μs, American 75μs). In i.c. form the detector multiplier circuit can provide half-wave or full-wave detection.

In Fig. 1(b), a half-wave detector, the average value of the output current in R_L is proportional to the frequency deviation of the input signal. The full-wave version (more complex, but less affected by noise) is given in Fig.1(c) and uses three, instead of two, pairs of differential long-tail transistors, but is similar in action.

The coincidence detector is becoming popular with i.cs in f.m. sets because the setting up of the detector involves the adjustment of only a single external coil, while giving performance similar to the more traditional, but more difficult to set up, Foster-Seeley and ratio detectors. Besides decreasing assembly and alignment time, the coincidence detector reduces the number of external passive components required.

TAA 661

One example of an i.f. amplifier using a coincidence detector is the SGS TAA661 which incorporates 25 transistors and 18 resistors in a single silicon chip. It is housed in a 14-lead dual-in-line package and includes a three-stage limiter amplifier,

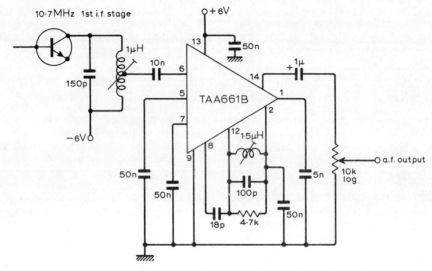

Fig. 2. Typical circuit using the TAA661 f.m. i.f. amplifier and coincidence detector.

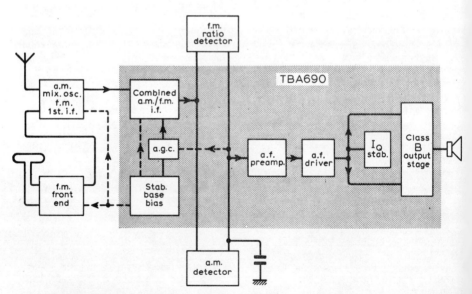

Fig. 3. How the Mullard TBA690 integrated circuit incorporates in a single package all stages of an a.m. /f.m. portable 9V receiver except the f.m. front end, the a.m. /f.m. input stage and the a.m. and f.m. detectors.

an f.m. detector and an emitter-follower audio buffer pre-amplifier, with an internal voltage regulator circuit permitting operation on rail supplies from 6 to 18V. How simply it can be used in practice is demonstrated in Fig.2 which shows the practical circuit for taking the output from a discrete component 10.7MHz f.m. first i.f. amplifier stage and delivering a.f. to the volume control.

TBA 690

The TAA661 is for f.m. only. Some domestic receivers covering f.m. also incorporate a.m. This points to a different line of i.c. development characterized by the Mullard TBA690. This i.c., in a 16-pin plastic dual-in-line package, comprises the functions within the shaded area of Fig.3, and can be seen to contain everything except the f.m. front end, the f.m. first i.f. (which can be switched to operate as a mixer oscillator on a.m.) and the f.m. and a.m. detectors. The integrated audio amplifier in the TBA690 can provide 500mW into an 8 Ω speaker on a 9V battery, although the supply can be anything from 4.5 to 9V. The quiescent current drain on the battery is only 22mA; this is comparable with discrete device designs. (A companion i.c., the TBA700, can operate from 4.5 to 12V on the rail and at 12V can supply an output of 1.5W into 8 Ω.)

It is not immediately evident from Fig.3 that the TBA690 does not of itself supply the selectivity provided in a discrete-component receiver by the r.f. front end tuned circuits and the fixed tuned i.f. circuits. In the arrangement of Fig.3, the r.f. selectivity is provided by the separate external input blocks, and the i.f. selectivity is provided by lumped *LC* or ceramic filter circuits between the a.m. mixer oscillator/f.m. first i.f. and the i.c. input. Equally the two detectors call for external tuned *LC* transformers. A new i.c. has just been announced (CA3089, see Literature Received) which combines the following functions: i.f. amplifier,

quadrature detector a.f. pre-amp,. with outputs for a.g.c., a.f.c.. muting (squelch) and tuning meter.

Stereo decoders

One area where monolithic i.c. techniques lend themselves is in stereo decoders. An example of this is the Siemens TBA450. Of the three standard decoder systems (matrix, switch and envelope), the TBA450 uses the matrix decoding system outlined diagrammatically in Fig.4. The output from a standard f.m. front end is taken after the detector, but without de-emphasis applied, and fed into three filters which separate the M (mono L + R) signal below 15kHz, the S (stereo L-R) signal from 23-53kHz, and the pilot signal at 19kHz. The pilot signal is frequency doubled to 38kHz and then controls a synchronous a.m. demodulator while the M and S signals are matrixed to give independent outputs of the stereo left and right audio signals. The same system is employed in the TBA450. In this circuit the bandpass amplifiers are active filters which do not use inductances.

Phase-locked-loop

The phase-locked-loop technique referred to in the last article on a.m. receivers offers a way of avoiding the fixed tuned i.f. filters of the f.m. receiver. Fig.5(a) shows the functional p.l.l. sections in the Signetics NE561B linear integrated circuit, which will provide a demodulated audio output if fed directly with the 10.7MHz output from a conventional f.m. mixer without any 10.7MHz tuned circuits. The tuning element in the circuit is a voltage controlled relaxation oscillator whose frequency is determined by non-inductive components. The oscillator is designed so that the operating frequency can be varied over a limited range by a d.c. bias voltage. If the oscillator is rough-tuned near to the 10.7MHz and its output is applied to the phase comparator, the comparator will give an output determined by the frequency and phase deviation of the v.c.o. from the input signal. This comparator output is amplified and filtered and fed back round the loop through the limiter to adjust the

art develops it is possible that the local oscillator too can be dispensed with.

The multiplier feeding the amplifier A_3 in Fig.5(a) is an additional a.m. detector that enables the NE561B to be switched to a.m. to provide an a.m./f.m. system. For

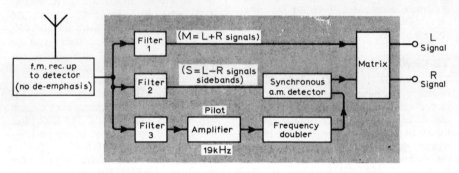

Filter 1 = low pass   Filter 2 = bandpass round 38kHz   Filter 3 = bandpass round 19kHz

Fig. 4. Stereo decoder integrated circut block diagram of matrix decoder system.

v.c.o. frequency to bring it into frequency and phase step with the f.m. input. Thus the oscillator tracks the input signal and produces a strong continuous signal even if the input is discontinuous or noisy.

So far the circuit has produced a cleaned up, greatly amplified, copy of the input f.m. signal without using inductances. But the main interest of the circuit to us is that within the phase comparator loop an output signal has been obtained which is dependent on the carrier shift. Apart from its use to lock the v.c.o. onto the carrier, it also represents the audio output of the demodulation system, because the amplitude of the loop control signal is proportional to the carrier frequency deviation . . . which is just the f.m. modulation. This enables the NE561B to be set up in a simple system such as Fig.5(b) to replace the complete 10.7MHz i.f. strip up to the f.m. detector. As yet, phase-locked-loop i.cs operating directly at the f.m. broadcasting frequencies around 100MHz are not practicable with existing monolithic technologies, but as the

this the a.m. is fed directly at the broadcast frequency into terminal 4 and the v.c.o. locks onto the carrier; the system providing detected audio output at terminal 1.

Digital synthesis

Another approach to eliminating tuned circuits with i.cs is the digital frequency synthesizer, which combines the phase-locked-loop with a master crystal oscillator. Frequency synthesizer circuits have been designed that generate the required local oscillator frequencies for an a.m. and f.m. broadcast receiver. Selection of a station is accomplished by positioning switches to indicate the station's frequency. Fine tuning is not necessary. The receiver will not (for all practical purposes) drift, because the local oscillator is crystal controlled. Low-cost medium-scale integrated circuits (m.s.i.) are the building blocks of this. For a more detailed account of this design, consult J. Stinehelfer and J. Nichols?

A digital frequency synthesizer for an a.m. and f.m. receiver' in *I.E.E.E. Transactions on Broadcast and Television Receivers,* October 1969, Vol.BTR-15, No.3, pp 235-243.

Thick film hybrid

Instead of packaging i.c. chips in multilead . packages and supplying them to set manufacturers to mount with passive components, such as resistors and

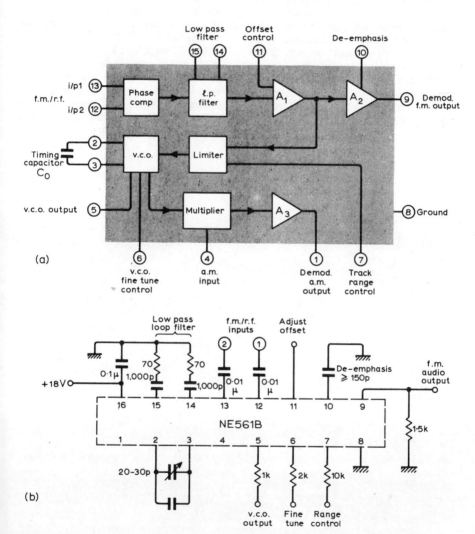

Fig. 5. Phase-locked-loop integrated circuit (Signetics NE561B) enabling complete inductorless substitute for conventional f.m. i.f. strip plus f.m. detector. (a) Internal functional sections of i.c., (b) connection as 10.7MHz a.m. /f.m. i.f. strip up to volume control.

capacitors, on a printed circuit board, we are already seeing a logical development in which semiconductor manufacturers are themselves mounting the chips in thick film hybrids with the passive components to complete their functions printed and fired on the ceramic substrates. This produces a neat microcircuit suitable for plugging into sockets on the printed circuit board (which now tends to become merely an interconnection network between the microcircuits and the large non-integratable components) and will remove many of the servicing problems found with discrete components or even linear monolithics soldered into position. With new subminiature i.f. transformers, about 5mm square, it is now possible to mount them directly onto thick film hybrids.

Conclusions

Much is happening in the application of i.cs to domestic f.m. receivers, and developments are taking place along several different lines at once. It is difficult to see how things will finally develop, but in the not-very-distant future we can expect to find the set makers indicating a preference which will show itself by semiconductor manufacturers beginning to 'second source' some items.

CHAPTER 12

Television receivers

In the 1960s transistors ousted valves from most circuit positions in domestic television receivers and now we are seeing linear microcircuits in their turn displacing transistors.

Although the U.S.A. has led the world in development of military and industrial i.cs, Western Europe has led in consumer i.cs (at least in monolithics, since in hybrids Japan has forged ahead). In Europe the main stream of i.c. development for television receivers has come from Western Germany with devices from Valvo (Philips), Siemens, Telefunken, and Intermetall (I.T.T.). Plessey in the U.K., S.G.S. in Italy and Secosem in France have also entered the field, while across the Atlantic Motorola, R.C.A., Texas Instruments and Fairchild are active.

To date the different semiconductor manufacturers have tended to adopt different approaches to partitioning the television receiver for linear i.c. substitution. As a result, second source supplies are not usually available to the set maker.

Good receiver partitioning aims at using the advantages of monolithic techniques up to a point where the replacement cost of any microcircuit is not prohibitive. A single microcircuit covering

all the electronics of the receiver is possible but economically prohibitive. It looks as if the number of microcircuits in a receiver will ultimately settle at between four and eight.

Until now linear i.cs have been most widely used in the sound channel, the post-video-detector signal processing, and the colour decoder. Limited frequency, voltage and power handling capabilities have restricted their applications in other areas. An understanding of the problems of the change-over to i.cs might well be helped by a study of the book 'Transistor Television Receivers' (Iliffe Books, 1963).

Sound channel

A natural development of the early op-amp linear i.c. was an amplifier microcircuit which gave the typical 66dB voltage gain needed in an f.m. intercarrier sound i.f. strip (200kHz bandwidth round 6MHz). The Mullard TAA350, with four current-driven, balanced, long-tail pairs giving efficient limiting and high a.m. rejection, was an example of this.

Fig. 1 (a) is a practical circuit (from the Pye 691 single-standard 625-line colour chassis) using the TAA350. The input is from an AA119 intercarrier sound detector via two 6MHz tuned circuits.

Output is via an OA90 sound detector to a volume control and an a.f. amplifier.

It is relatively easy to integrate a detector stage into a monolithic amplifier, and we find many commercial examples of this such as the Mullard TAA380, Plessey SL432A and Telefunken TAA930. All the basic f.m. detector types (discriminator, ratio, quadrature, differential peak, pulse counting and phase locked loop) have been tried. Anyone interested in the merits (or demerits) of the different detector systems should consult 'A Comparison of Integrated-circuit Television Sound Systems by L. Blaser and D. Long in *I.E.E.E. Transactions on Broadcast and Television*

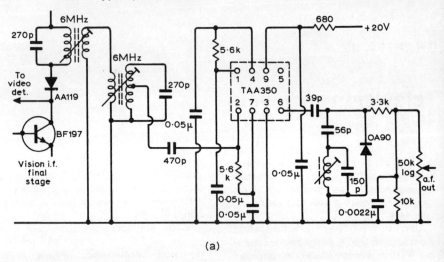

(a)

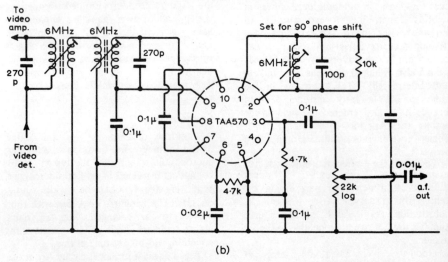

(b)

Fig. 1. Typical sound channel microcircuits. (a) Connections used with the Mullard TAA350 amplifier-limiter; (b) use of the TAA570 with integral detector.

Receivers, Feb., 1971, Vol. BTR-17, No. 1, pp. 35-43.

The long-tail pair makes it simple to vary voltage gain by varying the d.c. bias voltage on the base of one of the transistors of the pair, and we find a group of amplifier-limiter-detector i.cs with a d.c. volume control facility that enables the volume control potentiometer to be located some distance from the microcircuit. Typical of this type of i.c. are the Mullard TAA450 and TAA570 (Plessey pin-compatible SAA570), Siemens TBA120, and SGS TBA261. Fig. 1 (b) shows how the TAA570 has been used in the Pye 169/769 monochrome (625-line only) television chassis. Sound i.f. input comes via two 6MHz tuned circuits from the video detector, detection is by a single-tuned quadrature detector, and the audio output drives a two-stage valve amplifier. (The remote d.c. volume control available at pin 4 of the TAA570 has not been used in this case.)

Extra transistors are easy to fabricate in monoliths, so that the next development was to add an audio pre-amplifier stage to the limiter amplifier. This extra stage you will find in the Mullard TAA640, TAA750 and TBA480, and in the RCA3065.

Two audio stages (a pre-amplifier and driver) appear in such amplifier-limiter microcircuits as the SGS TBA581 (to drive class AB complementary transistor power output stages) and TBA591 (for class A transistor or valve output).

All the intercarrier sound i.cs described above require some form of external audio amplifier to complete the drive to the loudspeaker. These outboard audio amplifiers are still usually discrete transistor or valve designs, but microcircuit versions are available.

Monolithic audio amplifiers up to 3W output are now fairly common. Typical examples are the Telefunken TAA900 (2W) and SGS TAA621 (3W). By suitable heat-sinking, conventional monolithic designs can be pushed up to 5W, and we are already seeing new designs (e.g. from Sony) capable of 20W r.m.s. output.

Thick film add-on audio power amplifiers from 3-50W output are now produced by many Japanese firms such as Mitsubishi, N.E.C., Sanken, Sanyo and Toshiba, and will compete strongly with monoliths.

One interesting development that seems to point the way to the final solution to integrating into a single package the whole intercarrier sound channel is the SGS monolith TBA631, which combines the functions of limiter-amplifier, detector and 3W audio amplifier into a single chip with an integral heatsink.

Jungle chips

The post-video-detector circuitry of the television receiver has received much attention from i.c. manufacturers. It has been found possible to integrate in one chip the following video signal processing functions: video pre-amplification, keyed a.g.c. detection, a.g.c. amplification for both tuner and vision i.f. control, noise cancellation for a.g.c. and sync. circuits, sync. separation, automatic horizontal sync. and, finally, vertical sync. pulse separation. This video signal processing i.c. is variously known as the 'signal processing circuit' or, affectionately and obviously, as the 'jungle chip'.

The best known example is the Mullard TAA700 (now superseded by the TBA550) (with the pin-compatible Plessey SAA700). The circuit is too extensive to set out in detail here but Mullard can supply data to prospective users.

The TAA700 is designed for TV receivers equipped with transistors or valves in the deflection and video output stages, with n-p-n transistors in the tuner and i.f. amplifier, and with negative modulation. It works on a nominal 12V d.c. supply rail.

Sound/vision i.f.

Sound/vision i.fs present special problems in applying i.cs because the first i.f. stage must have a.g.c., and the requirement for many tuned bandpass and rejector circuits has tended to give the monolithic i.c., for sound/vision i.f. only applications, no advantage over discrete transistor assemblies. Away back in 1967 Fairchild brought out the μ A 717 for just such a purpose, but it was never widely adopted at least on this side of the Atlantic.

detector, a 12dB video pre-amp., an impulse noise limiter, keyed a.g.c. with noise immunity, delayed a.g.c. for the tuner, buffered automatic fine tuning for varicap tuner control, separate sound i.f. amplification, sound carrier detector, 4.5MHz sound intercarrier pre-amplifier and isolated zener reference diode for

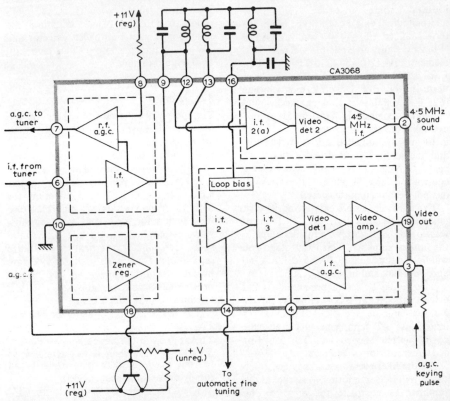

Fig. 2. Combined sound/vision i.f. microcircuit type CA3068.

An i.c. combining the sound/vision i.f. amplifier with some later stages of the receiver can, however, make integration an economic proposition. One interesting example of this is the RCA CA3068 shown in section block diagram in Fig. 2.

The CA3068 provides a high gain (75dB typical) 45MHz wideband i.f. amplifier with 50dB a.g.c., a video

regulated voltage supply. The connection diagram of Fig. 2 illustrates the simplicity of use of this i.c., particularly when the needs of the serviceman are remembered.

Another interesting approach to sound/vision i.f. microcircuitry was described in 'A Thick-film Television Video I.F. Amplifier Using Compatible Components' by R. Weber and J.

100

Prabhakar in *I.E.E.E. Transactions on Broadcast and Television Receivers*, Nov. 1967, Vol.BTR13, No.3, pp.7-12. In this, thick film techniques were used with printed capacitors and surface mounted toroidal coils, both capacitors and coils being adjustable on test by abrasive (powder jet blast) techniques. While this approach has not been widely adopted, it has attractions because it can produce a pre-aligned plug-in i.c. requiring no adjustment by the set maker or serviceman.

Tuner

The frequencies (up to 900MHz) handled by the tuner are well beyond current monolithic i.c. capabilities. Hybrid (thick or thin film) techniques show some promise as explained in 'The New Thick-film Hybrid Integrated Circuit Module for V.H.F. Television Tuners' by K. Williams in *I.E.E.E. Transactions on Broadcast and Television Receivers*, July, 1968, Vol. BTR-14, No. 2, pp. 111-115. Plugged into the appropriate passive tuning networks, the resultant i.c. provides all the active circuitry for a v.h.f. tuner which is competitive with discrete device assemblies on the score of both performance and cost.

Most new European television receivers are now varicap-tuned, and although it has not been possible to produce a commercially viable tuner i.c., several firms have produced a self-contained voltage regulator i.c. to provide the very stable 30V or so required for varicap tuning. Typical of these is the Mullard TAA550 and Telefunken TBA940.

Colour television receivers

Some of the microcircuits described earlier, such as the tuner-varicap regulated supply, the sound/vision i.f., the sound channel, and the video processing jungle i.c., can be used in monochrome or colour sets. But a special breed of microcircuits has also been developed for colour signal processing.

There are several different approaches to the problem of handling colour signals with i.cs. The Mullard set of i.cs consists of the TBA500 video combination, TBA510 chrominance combination, TBA520 (TBA990) colour demodulator, TBA530 RGB matrix and TBA540 colour subcarrier combination. Space prevents a full description here of the internal circuitry and design problems of this family which is constantly being updated. However, for conventional colour difference drive to the c.r.t. grids, a practical system uses four of the i.cs . . . the TBA 500, 510 520 and 540 . . . . as shown in Fig. 3(a). Essentially, the luminance (Y) input to the TBA500 (which could come from the TAA700 described earlier) is amplified, delayed and fed into the Y amplifier to drive the c.r.t. cathodes. The TBA510 takes the chrominance input, centred about 4.43MHz, separates off the chrominance (R−Y, B−Y) information and feeds it via a 64 s glass delay line to the colour synchronous demodulator, TBA520. At the same time it isolates the 4.43MHz colour subcarrier information and feeds it to the TBA540 where it controls the 4.43MHz crystal carrier reinsertion local oscillator to produce a correct phase and frequency output to feed the synchronous demodulator TBA520, also taking into account the PAL phase reversal on alternate lines. In the TBA520, the demodulated R−Y and B−Y inputs are combined (matrixed) to give a G−Y signal. The three colour-difference signals are then fed through separate discrete-component amplifiers to the c.r.t. grids. Where an RGB drive to the separate c.r.t. cathodes is desired, the fifth i.c. of the set, the TBA530 is interposed between the luminance and colour-difference outputs on the one hand and the c.r.t. RGB drive amplifiers on the other as shown in Fig. 3(b).

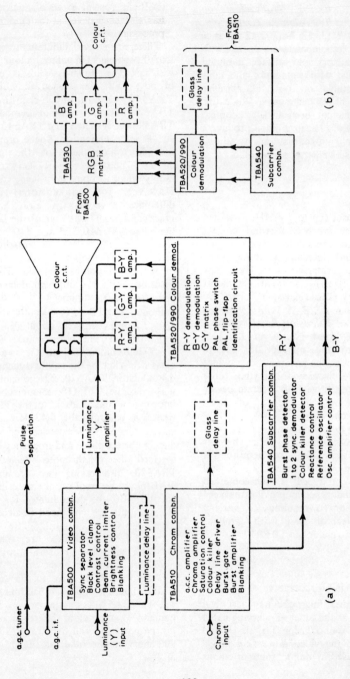

Fig. 3. Using the Mullard TBA500 series in colour receivers. (a) Colour difference arrangement; (b) RGB drive.

102

Interesting alternative approaches to colour signal processing can be found in 'Integrated M.T.O.S. Circuits for Colour TV Applications' by M. M. Mitchell and W. Sheets in *I.E.E.E. Transactions on Broadcast and Television Receivers,* July, 1968, Vol. BTR-14, No. 2, pp. 28-33, and in 'Colour Command—A Digital Method for Extracting the Colour Information so far, but thick-film hybrids are beginning to offer strong competition. Fig. 4 shows in block form the use of six thick-film i.cs which provide most of the circuitry for a 17in v.h.f. receiver designed by Tokyo Sanyo Ltd. Using an insulated-metal-substrate, Sanyo can meet the high voltage and power requirements of output stages without separate amplifiers. As a

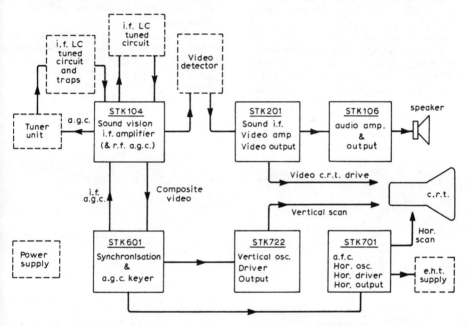

Fig. 4. Six thick film hybrid microcircuits from Sanyo provide most of the circuitry for this 17in receiver.

from the N.T.S.C. Signal' by R. Weber and T. T. Fu in the same journal, July 1968, Vol. BTR-14, No. 2, pp. 52-57.

Going back to Fig. 3, it will be seen that the drive circuits to the c.r.t. are discrete component, transistor or valve. Thick film hybrids are now available to replace these, as for example in the 'Accucircuit' plug-in microcircuits produced by RCA.

Future of i.cs in television receivers

Monolithic i.cs predominate in the microcircuits for TV receivers described result, the count of 25 transistors, 246 other parts and 553 solder joints for conventional discrete assembly is reduced to 6 i.cs, 58 other parts and 198 solder joints. For fuller discussion, you should consult 'Development of All-i.c. 17in Black-and-white Line-operated TV Receiver' by Sadao Kondo, et. al. in *I.E.E.E. Transactions on Broadcast and Television Receivers,* May, 1971, Vol. BTR-17, No. 2, pp. 98-104.

The shape of things to come can also be seen in the Matsushita (Panasonic) pocket-size receiver using eight thick film hybrids providing the functions sound i.f. and detector, audio and a.g.c., vision i.f., video detector and amplifier, sync. separator and a.f.c., vertical deflection, horizontal deflection and power supply filtering.

Finally we can expect to see a mixing of i.c. technologies as foreshadowed in a colour TV design developed at the Kansai Electronic Industry Development Centre in Japan and organized by five TV manufacturers, seven component producers, four universities and two institutes in the Osaka area. While the design uses a discrete u.h.f. tuner, the v.h.f. tuner uses a thin film r.f. amplifier and a monolithic mixer/oscillator. The 3W audio amplifier is monolithic, as are the vertical and horizontal oscillators. In the colour section, thick film is used for the chrominance bandpass amplifier, the chrominance demodulators, the matrix pre-amplifier and the subcarrier reactance oscillator, with monolithics for the colour killer, and colour burst amplifier. Both thick and thin film are used in the colour phase detector circuit.

Development is now so rapid that a pundit in the U.S.A. has been quoted as going on record that in five years time 75% of the circuitry of the televison set will be integrated in only three i.cs.

Index